To Set a Country Free

*An account derived from the exhibition
in the Library of Congress commemorating
the 200th anniversary of
American independence.*

*Opened on April 24, 1975, the
175th anniversary of
the establishment of the Library of Congress*

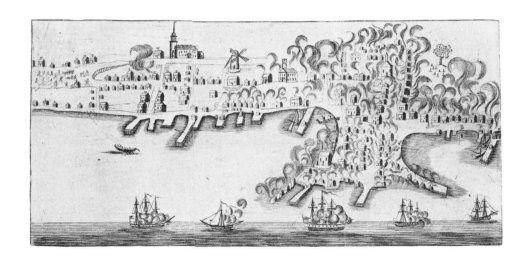

LIBRARY OF CONGRESS WASHINGTON 1975

To Set a Country Free

Errata

Page 4. The caption for the illustration on page 4 should read:
*George III. Painting by Allan Ramsay. National Portrait
Gallery, London. On display in the exhibit is a
mezzotint engraving of George III by William Pether, 1762,
after an engraving by Thomas Frye. LC-USZ62-7819.*

Page 39. Paragraph 2, lines 8 and 9:
January 3, 1776 *should read*

FRONTISPIECE:

This engraving in An Impartial History of the War in America,
Between Great Britain and the United States *(Boston, 1782),
depicts the bombardment by Henry Mowat, commanding the
British man-of-war* Canceaux, *off Falmouth (later Portland),
Maine. More than half of the town was destroyed during the
course of this eight- or nine-hour attack. LC-USZ62-45238*

LIBRARY OF CONGRESS CATALOGING IN PUBLICATION DATA

United States. Library of Congress.
   To set a country free.

   Catalog.
   Supt. of Docs. no.: LC 1.2: C83
   1. United States—History—Revolution, 1775–1783—
Exhibitions. I. Title.
E289.U55 1975   973.3'074'0153   74-8556
ISBN 0-8444-0126-9

Foreword

In September 1774, 56 men from 12 of Great Britain's North American colonies met at Carpenter's Hall in Philadelphia to discuss the troubled relations between the colonies and Great Britain. This meeting, the First Continental Congress, was the formal beginning of the united American movement toward independence.

To celebrate the momentous events that continued through the next nine years, the Library of Congress has prepared an exhibition taken, with only three exceptions, from its own rich and varied resources in United States history.

Among the earliest actions of the First Continental Congress was a resolution thanking the Library Company of Philadelphia for the use of its library. Congressional need for books continued, and in 1800, when the seat of government was to be moved to Washington, the Sixth Congress provided "for the purchase of such books as may be necessary for the use of Congress . . . and for fitting up a suitable apartment for containing them."

Those words, in effect, established the Library of Congress; the opening date of this exhibition marks the 175th anniversary of their enactment into law.

This volume is based upon the exhibition; many of the materials displayed serve as illustrations to the text. *To Set a Country Free* is one in a continuing series of Library of Congress publications designed to further the public's acquaintance with both the story of the American Revolution and the Library's extensive holdings in Americana. The title is taken from Thomas Paine's *American Crisis*: "We fight not to enslave, but to set a country free, and to make room upon the earth for honest men to live in."

For this exhibition the Public Records Office, London, has lent the Olive Branch Petition. I take this opportunity to express the thanks of all Americans for this act of generosity. The Library is grateful also to the National Archives for lending the Charles Thomson drawing of the Great Seal of the United States and the 1778 Treaty of Alliance between France and the United States.

ELIZABETH HAMER KEGAN
Assistant Librarian of Congress

Prelude to War

George III. Mezzotint engraving by William Pether, 1762, after an engraving by Thomas Frye. LC-USZ62-15553

Royal proclamation of 1762, announcing the end of hostilities between Great Britain on the one side and France and Spain on the other, thus concluding what was known in Europe as the Seven Years' War and in America as the French and Indian War.

Perhaps the most recurrent phrase used to describe the pre-1763 attitude of Great Britain toward her colonies beyond the Atlantic is "salutary neglect." This phrase conveys the notion that in the first half of the 18th century Britain was so preoccupied with consolidating the results of the Glorious Revolution of 1688, with various European wars, and with the rapidly occurring changes in domestic, social, and economic conditions that she paid little attention to her colonies in America. Far from suffering from this inattention, the colonies during those years matured politically and prospered economically. Some enjoyed virtual self-government, and the experience of successfully running their own affairs convinced many colonists that autonomy had been a blessing and should be a right.

By the KING,

A PROCLAMATION,

Declaring the Ceſſation of Arms, as well by Sea as Land, agreed upon between His Majeſty, the Moſt Chriſtian King, and the Catholick King, and enjoining the Obſervance thereof.

GEORGE R.

HEREAS Preliminaries for reſtoring Peace were ſigned at *Fontainebleau*, on the Third Day of this Inſtant *November*, by the Miniſters of Us, the Moſt Chriſtian King, and the Catholick King : And whereas for the putting an End to the Calamities of War, as ſoon and as far as may be poſſible, it has been agreed between Us, His Moſt Chriſtian Majeſty, and His Catholick Majeſty, as follows ; that is to ſay,

That as ſoon as the Preliminaries ſhall be ſigned and ratified, all Hoſtilities ſhould ceaſe at Sea and at Land.

And to prevent all Occaſions of Complaints and Diſputes which might ariſe upon account of Ships, Merchandizes, and other Effects, which might be taken at Sea ; it has been alſo mutually agreed, That the Ships, Merchandizes, and Effects, which ſhould be taken in the *Channel*, and in the *North Seas*, after the Space of Twelve Days, to be computed from the Ratification of the preſent Preliminary Articles ; and that all Ships, Merchandizes, and Effects, which ſhould be taken after Six Weeks from the ſaid Ratification, beyond the *Channel*, the *Britiſh Seas*, and the *North Seas*, as far as the *Canary Iſlands* incluſively, whether in the Ocean, or *Mediterranean* ; and for the Space of Three Months, from the ſaid *Canary Iſlands* to the *Equinoctial Line* or *Equator* ; and for the Space of Six Months, beyond the ſaid *Equinoctial Line* or *Equator*, and in all other Places of the World, without any Exception, or other more particular Diſtinction of Time or Place, ſhould be reſtored on both Sides.

And whereas the Ratifications of the ſaid Preliminary Articles, in due Form, were exchanged at *Verſailles*, by the Plenipotentiaries of Us, of the Moſt Chriſtian King, and of the Catholick King, on the Twenty ſecond of this Inſtant *November*, from which Day the ſeveral Terms above-mentioned of Twelve Days, of Six Weeks, of Three Months, and of Six Months, for the Reſtitution of all Ships, Merchandizes, and other Effects, taken at Sea, are to be computed.

We have thought fit, by and with the Advice of Our Privy Council, to notify the ſame to all Our loving Subjects: and We do declare, That Our Royal Will and Pleaſure is, and We do hereby ſtrictly Charge and Command all Our Officers, both at Sea and Land, and all other Our Subjects whatſoever, to forbear all Acts of Hoſtility, either by Sea or Land, againſt His Moſt Chriſtian Majeſty, and His Catholick Majeſty, Their Vaſſals, or Subjects, from and after the reſpective Times above-mentioned, and under the Penalty of incurring Our higheſt Diſpleaſure.

Given at Our Court at *Saint James's*, the Twenty ſixth Day of *November*, in the Third Year of Our Reign, and in the Year of Our Lord 1762.

God ſave the King.

LONDON:

Printed by *Mark Baſkett*, Printer to the King's moſt Excellent Majeſty ; and by the Aſſigns of *Robert Baſkett*. 1762.

The Seven Years' War (1756–63) awakened Americans to the reality of their political subordination to Britain. Precipitated by a quarrel between Britain and France over their respective boundaries in North America, the war was marked by an unprecedented amount of major fighting in the New World. The fortunes of war awarded Britain the vast domain of French Canada. For the first time Britain's attention was focused on her colonies, and she saw many things which she did not like. The challenge of administering a much-enlarged empire now coincided with the desire to reform the governance of the colonies and to thwart what were perceived to be aspirations to autonomy. In 1763 King George III issued a proclamation, forbidding the colonists to settle west of the Allegheny Mountains, and the next year Parliament passed the Currency Act and the Sugar Act, both of which impinged on American freedom of action.

The Currency Act forbade the colonies south of New England to issue legal tender paper money. (New England had been restrained from such emissions in 1751.) Unfortunately for Britain, the act coincided with a postwar economic depression and in many quarters was blamed for causing it. Opposition to the Currency Act was so persistent and pervasive that in 1773 it was modified, though not entirely to the colonists' satisfaction. For many Americans the Currency Act symbolized a British effort to stifle their economic growth. Although most historians have discounted the notion that the Revolution was primarily caused by Britain's desire to throttle an American economy that was becoming increasingly competitive, none have denied that economic conflict was present throughout the 1760's and 1770's and that it exacerbated the political quarrel.

The Sugar Act imposed unwelcome economic controls upon the American economy, principally by bringing under tighter regulation the trade in molasses, the staple of the colonists' important rum industry. But the Sugar Act was much more than an irritant to distilling interests. The duties which it laid on molasses were imposed by Parliament on Americans without their consent and, therefore, the colonists evoked the constitutional argument that taxation without representation was wrong and tyrannical. These protests, however, were but faint adumbrations of the fury aroused the next year by Parliament's passage of the Stamp Act.

Unlike the Sugar Act, which some Americans condoned because it was, in part at least, an exercise of Parliament's acknowledged power to regulate the commerce of the empire, the Stamp Act laid duties purely to raise revenue. Americans, taught to believe that the taking of one's property without his consent was tantamount to slavery (the enormity of which they witnessed daily), responded to the Stamp Act as if it were a declaration of war. Up and down the colonies stamp distributors were forced to resign, frequently with violence, or threats of it, to their persons and property. Supporters of the act were paraded through the streets by mobs. Stamped paper was hurled into bonfires.

An assembly, the so-called Stamp Act Congress, met in New York in the fall of 1765 and sent petitions to the king and Parliament. Learned and eloquent statements of American rights like Daniel Dulany's *Considerations on the Propriety of Imposing Taxes in the British Colonies* issued from the presses.

Charles Townshend, chancellor of the exchequer in the administration of William Pitt the elder, 1766–67. Contemporary engraving by [John?] Miller. LC-USZ62-33231

John Dickinson. Engraving by Benoît L. Prevost, probably in 1781, after a life drawing by Pierre Eugene DuSimitière. LC-USZ62-26777

The initial violence was soon directed into other means of protest by the Sons of Liberty, essentially middle class groups who were the points of the revolutionary party's spear until independence was declared. The method of opposition eventually hit upon to force Britain to repeal the Stamp Act was the nonimportation agreement, a device which pleased the conservative and the timid because it was nonviolent, the merchants because it allowed them a period in which to dispose of a glut of British goods in their hands, the mechanics and the manufacturing interests because it acted as a protective tariff against competing British wares, and the generality of the population because it promised to be an effective weapon. The nonimportation agreements were designed to make British manufacturers and their dependents, whose businesses they intentionally injured, advocates for America. Owing in part to the pressure which the British manufacturing interests exerted on Parliament, the Stamp Act was repealed in 1766.

Concurrently with its repeal, however, Parliament passed a Declaratory Act in which it portentiously announced its power to bind the colonists "in all cases whatsoever." The meaning of this declaration became clear in 1767, when Parliament laid another series of taxes—the so-called Townshend Duties—on goods imported into America. Once again, pamphleteers declaimed against the tyranny of taxation without representation, with John Dickinson gaining an international reputation for his lucid statement of the American case in *Letters From a Farmer in Pennsylvania*. Once again, nonimportation agreements were established in the various colonies. But the Townshend Duties were not as easily subverted as the Stamp Act had been. Many in Britain denounced the repeal of that statute

8

This British cartoon, endorsing the government's about-face on the Stamp Act, followed hard on the heels of its repeal by Parliament in 1766. The bannered representations of newspaper stamps are incorrectly priced; an exact copy of an actual stamp would have opened the engraver to a charge of forgery, at that time a capital offense. LC-USZ62-21264

THE REPEAL

OR THE FUNERAL OF MISS AME-STAMP

THE Hero of this Print is the gentle Mr. *Stamper*, who is carrying to the Family Vault his favourite Child, in a Coffin, Miss AME-STAMP, about 12 Months old. *Anti-Sejanus*, who reads the Burial Service, is the first in the Proceffion.—After him follow Two Pillars of the Law, fupporting Two Black Flags : on which are the ufual Stamps, confifting of the *White Rofe* united with the *Thiftle*, fuppofed to have been originally contrived on the *Tenth of June*. The expreffive Motto of *Semper eadem* is preferved : but the Price of the Stamp is changed to *Three Farthing* , which the *Budget* explains : and the *fmall Numbers*, which are pointed at, are too contemptible to deferve Notice *by the Majority*. The Chief Mourner, *Sejanus*, follows Mr. *Stamper*. Then Two remarkable Perfonages , the celebrated *Weaver* and Lord *Gawkee* : after them *Jemmy Twitcher*, with his Friend and Partner, Lord H—————. Two B—————s conclude the Proceffion. Upon the Fore Ground are two large Bales of Black Cloth and Stamps returned from *America*.

The unhappy Gang are feparated from the joyous Scene that is oppofite, on the other Side of the River *Thames*. where, along the Shore, are *Open Warehoufes* for the Goods of different Manufacturing Towns now fhipping for *America*. In the River are three Firft-rate Ships, the *Rockingham*, the *Grafton*, and the *Conway*. Among the Goods fhipping off, is a large Cafe, which is wrote upon a *Statue of Mr. Pitt* : this is heaving on board a Boat *Number 250*. There is another Boat under the Firft-rates, taking Goods in alfo ; and is *numberd* 1—————.—————*N. B.* The two Skeleton Heads, upon the Vault were Monfters born in the Rebellions of the Years 1715 and 1745.

9

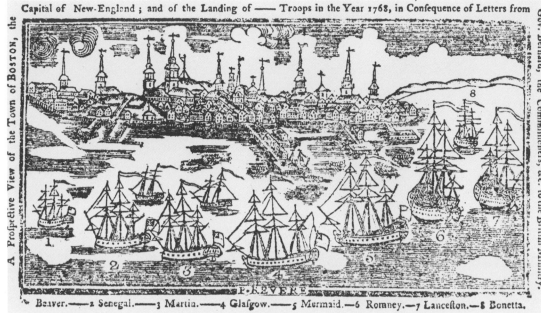

A Profpective View of the Town of BOSTON, the Capital of New-England; and of the Landing of ‹—› Troops in the Year 1768, in Confequence of Letters from Gov. Bernard, the Commiffioners, &c. to the Britifh Miniftry.

P·REVERE

1 Beaver.—2 Senegal.—3 Martin.—4 Glafgow.—5 Mermaid.—6 Romney.—7 Lanceston.—8 Bonetta.

from a Painting by Stuart.

The landing of the British troops in Boston in 1768—a response to colonial reaction to the administration of the Townshend Acts—was the subject of this woodcut by Paul Revere in Edes & Gill's North-American Almanack and Massachusetts Register *(Boston, 1770).* LC-USZ62-45559

Paul Revere at 78. Lithograph by William S. Pendleton in The New England Magazine *(October 1832), after an 1813 painting by Gilbert Stuart.* LC-USZ62-48400

as an act of appeasement which had encouraged American opposition to the Townshend Duties; were these now to be repealed, it was feared that the Americans would become ungovernable. This hardening of the British attitude increased as the revolutionary crisis deepened and finally turned into an intransigence which undermined all efforts at accommodation.

Another reason the Townshend Duties were not so swiftly repealed was the British annoyance at the Americans'— and particularly the Bostonians'—opposition to the Board of Customs Commissioners, which had been established in Boston to administer the duties. Americans viewed the commissioners and their understrappers as so many cormorants, sating themselves on the plunder of innocent American merchants. One historian, in fact, has described their activities as "customs racketeering." By 1768 the commissioners began to feel so threatened by the inhabitants of Boston that they called in British regulars to protect them. The folly of putting royal troops in the Puritan metropolis in a time of peace was soon manifest.

Animosity between citizens and soldiers seethed, and an affray in March 1770 provoked a detachment of redcoats to fire into a crowd of colonists, killing five.

Cried up as a "massacre" by Bostonians and exploited as such by patriot writers, the killings appeared to be one of the most alarming steps in what was widely viewed as a systematic British plan to enslave the colonies. This notion of a system—a design of despotism—seeped into the colonists' consciousness from the writings of British pundits and journalists who admired and often borrowed the rhetoric of the heroes of England's Commonwealth period. The conviction of a British conspiracy against American liberties sent down deeper roots as the years passed. It finally undermined the trust and confidence in the British government to such a degree that a continued political connection was impossible.

In 1770 every Townshend Duty except that on tea was repealed. The colonists responded by lifting their non-importation agreement on every article except tea. A calm

Frederick, Lord North, prime minister of Great Britain, 1770–82. Engraving in The London Magazine *(October 1779) where it is observed that "he has involved the nation year after year, deeper and deeper in the fruitless and fatal American war."* LC-USZ62-45503

The Boston Massacre, March 5, 1770. Engraved by Paul Revere. LC-USZ62-35522

Americans throwing the Cargoes of the Tea Ships into the River, at Boston. *Engraving, in W. D. Cooper,* History of North America *(London, 1789).* LC-USZ62-48565

seemed to descend over America, to the despair of activists like Samuel Adams of Boston, who tried to keep the revolutionary cauldron boiling by persuading the Boston Town Meeting in 1772 to establish an intracolonial committee of correspondence, which reported all British violations of American rights, real and imaginary, and which quickly led to the development of a network of similar committees among all the colonies. The passage by the British Parliament in 1773 of the Tea Act gave Adams and his newly constituted cohorts plenty to correspond about.

Engraving of Samuel Adams in An Impartial History of the War in America *(London, 1780). The "Plan of the Reduction of Canada," in Adams' left hand, was actually the work of Benedict Arnold. It was mistakenly attributed to Adams by the English because of his well-known enthusiasm for such an undertaking.* LC-USZ62-45248

A Society of Patriotic Ladies at Edenton in North Carolina. *This mezzotint engraving, probably by Philip Dawe, was published in London in March 1775. It followed reports in the British press of colonial ladies emptying their household cannisters of tea.* LC-USZ62-12711

13

This act, which precipitated the final crisis between Britain and America, was designed to rescue the East India Company from threatened bankruptcy, by granting it the remission of duties on tea exported to America and by permitting it to sell tea in the colonies through its own network of agents, rather than at public auction, as it had previously been compelled to do. The result would have been to reduce the price of the company's teas in America below that of smuggled tea. These cutrate prices, it was feared in patriot circles, would tempt Americans to consume taxed tea, thereby acknowledging Britain's rights to tax them. The creation of a monopoly was also discerned in the design of the Tea Act and, accordingly, it evoked the opposition of American mechanics and manufacturing interests, who feared such a precedent.

The most spectacular opposition to the Tea Act occurred at Boston, where on a cold December night a group of Sons of Liberty, disguised as Mohawk Indians, emptied 342 chests of East India Company tea into the harbor. British reprisals followed in the form of the "Intolerable Acts" which: (1) closed the port of Boston until the damages inflicted by the Tea Party were paid, (2) virtually annulled the Massachusetts charter, and (3) removed royal officials from the jurisdiction of provincial courts.

Other colonies were quick to see that what could be done to Massachusetts could be done to them. The Virginia House of Burgesses declared a fast day to stir sympathy for Boston. South Carolina shipped money and rice to the suffering city; Connecticut and New York sent sheep. Nearly everywhere the colonists closed ranks, and in response to an invitation from the Massachusetts House of Delegates, each colony, save badly divided Georgia, prepared to send delegates to a continental congress at Philadelphia in September 1774.

Tar and feathers being readied for a colonial customs official in January 1774. Wash drawing, by F. Godefroy, in Nicholas Ponce's Recueil d'estampes représentant les différents évenemens de la guerre ... (Paris, 1784?). LC-USZ62-39581

Another in a series of mezzotint engravings attributed to Philip Dawe. This one was inspired by the following announcement, published in New York on October 3, 1774:

The thanks of the *worthy* sons of liberty in solemn Congress assembled, were this night voted and unanimously allowed to be justly due to Mr. Jacob Vredenburgh, Barber, for his *firm spirited* and *patriotic conduct* in refusing to complete an operation, vulgarly called *Shaving*, which he had begun on the face of Captain John Crozer, Commander of the Empress of Russia, one of his Majesty's transports, now lying in the river, but most *fortunately* and *providentially* was informed of the identity of the gentleman's person, when he had about half finished the job.

It is most devoutly to be wished that all Gentlemen of the Razor will follow this wise, prudent, interesting and praiseworthy example....

LC-USZ62-17658

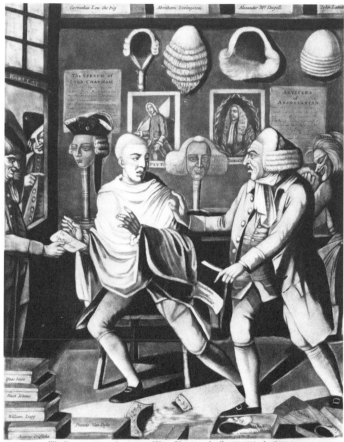

The PATRIOTICK BARBER of NEW YORK, or the CAPTAIN in the SUDS.

Plate III

The First Continental Congress

This imaginative engraving by Godefroy after Le Barbier of the First Continental Congress appeared in Hilliard d'Auberteuil's Essais historiques et politiques sur les Anglo-Américains *(Brussels, 1782). LC-USZ62-45328*

The First Continental Congress convened at Philadelphia on September 5, 1774. Offered the Pennsylvania State House by conservative leader Joseph Galloway, the delegates chose instead to meet in Carpenters' Hall, a move which, it was correctly thought, would be "highly agreeable to the mechanics and citizens in general." Among the delegates, representing every colony except Georgia, were John Sullivan of New Hampshire; the Adams cousins, John and Samuel, from Massachusetts; Silas Deane and Roger Sherman from Connecticut; Samuel Ward and Stephen Hopkins from Rhode Island; John Jay and James Duane from New York; William Livingston from New Jersey; Joseph Galloway and John Dickinson from Pennsylvania; Caesar Rodney from Delaware; Thomas Johnson and Samuel Chase from Maryland; George Washington and Patrick Henry from Virginia; William Hooper and Joseph Hewes from North Carolina; and Christopher Gadsden and John Rutledge from South Carolina.

The Congress accomplished as much as its supporters hoped and more than its opponents feared. It adopted a petition to the king, praying for a redress of grievances, and a Declaration of Rights, which incorporated most of the Whig positions advanced by colonial spokesmen like Jefferson, whose *Summary View of the Rights of British America* had appeared in August. The Congress resolved to employ the familiar weapon of a nonimportation, nonconsumption agreement, called the Continental Association, in an effort to wring concessions from the British. A respectful hearing was accorded Joseph Galloway's plan for an Anglo-American union, which envisioned an American legislature, constitutionally inferior to Parliament but with a veto power over its acts relating to America. Galloway's plan was rejected by the delegates, who placed their faith in the Continental Association. In the event that commercial coercion failed, as men like John Adams predicted it would, a second meeting of the Continental Congress was scheduled for the following May.

16

will consent to have no representative in assembly? That colony has as yet fixed no boundary to the westward. Their western counties, therefore, are of indefinite extent; some of them are actually seated many hundred miles from their eastern limits. Is it possible, then, that his majesty can have bestowed a single thought on the situation of those people, who, in order to obtain justice for injuries, however great or small, must, by the laws of that colony, attend their county court, at such a distance, with all their witnesses, monthly, till their litigation be determined? Or does his majesty seriously wish, and publish it to the world, that his subjects should give up the glorious right of representation, with all the benefits derived from that, and submit themselves the absolute slaves of his sovereign will? Or is it rather meant to confine the legislative body to their present numbers, that they may be the cheaper bargain whenever they shall become worth a purchase.

One of the articles of impeachment against Tresilian, and the other judges of Westminster Hall, in the reign of Richard the second, for which they suffered death, as traitors to their country, was, that they had advised the king that he might dissolve his parliament at any time; and succeeding kings have adopted the opinion of these unjust judges. Since the ~~reign~~ *of the Second William* ~~~~, however, *under whom* ~~in~~ the British constitution, ~~~~ was settled ~~~~, on its free and antient principles, neither his majesty, nor his ancestors, have exercised such a power of dissolution in the island of Great Britain; and when his majesty was petitioned, by the united voice of his people there, to dissolve the present parliament, who had become obnoxious to them, his ministers were heard to declare, in open parliament, that his majesty possessed no such power by the constitution.* But how different their language and his practice here! To declare, as their duty required, the known rights of their country, to oppose the usurpations of every foreign judicature, to disregard the imperious mandates of a minister or governor, have been the avowed causes of dissolving houses of representatives in America. But if such powers be,

* since this period the king has several times dissolved the parliament a few weeks before it's expiration, merely as an assertion of the right.

really vested in his majesty, can he suppose they are there placed to awe the members from such purposes as these? When the representative body have lost the confidence of their constituents, when they have notoriously made sale of their most valuable rights, when they have assumed to themselves powers which the people never put into their hands, then indeed their continuing in office becomes dangerous to the state, and calls for an exercise of the power of dissolution. Such being the causes for which the representative body should, and should not, be dissolved, will it not appear strange to an unbiassed observer, that that of Great Britain was not dissolved, while those of the colonies have repeatedly incurred that sentence?

But your majesty, or your governors, have carried this power beyond every limit known, or provided for, by the laws: After dissolving one house of representatives, they have refused to call another, so that, for a great length of time, the legislature provided by the laws has been out of existence. From the nature of things, every society must at all times possess within itself the sovereign powers of legislation. The feelings of human nature revolt against the supposition of a state so situated as that it may not in any emergency provide against dangers which perhaps threaten immediate ruin. While those bodies are in existence to whom the people have delegated the powers of legislation, they alone possess and may exercise those powers; but when they are dissolved by the lopping off one or more of their branches, the power reverts to the people, who may exercise it to unlimited extent, either assembling together in person, sending deputies, or in any other way they may think proper.* We forbear to trace consequences further; the dangers are conspicuous with which this practice is replete.

That we shall at this time also take notice of an error in the nature of our land holdings, which crept in at a very early period of our settlement. The introduction of the feudal tenures into the kingdom of England, though antient, is well enough understood to set this matter in a proper light. In the earlier ages of the Saxon settlement feudal holdings were

* insert "and the frame of government thus dissolved, should the people take upon them to lay the throne of your majesty prostrate, or to discontinue their connection with the British empire, none will be so bold as to decide against the right or the efficacy of such avulsion."

Marginalia in the author's hand on Thomas Jefferson's own copy of his Summary View of the Rights of British America, *printed in Williamsburg in August 1774 and intended as instructions to the Virginia delegation to the First Continental Congress.*

EXTRACTS

FROM THE

VOTES and PROCEEDINGS

OF THE

AMERICAN CONTINENTAL

CONGRESS,

HELD AT

PHILADELPHIA,

On the 5th of September, 1774.

CONTAINING

The BILL of RIGHTS, a Lift of GRIEVANCES,
Occasional RESOLVES, the Association, an Address
to the PEOPLE of Great-Britain, and a Memorial to
the Inhabitants of the British American Colonies.

PUBLISHED BY ORDER OF THE CONGRESS.

PHILADELPHIA: Printed.

HARTFORD: Re-Printed by EBEN. WATSON, near
the GREAT-BRIDGE.

John Adams. Engraving by John Norman in The Boston Magazine
(*February 1784*), *possibly adapted from an anonymous engraving
which appeared in London's* European Magazine *the previous
year. LC-USZ62-45280*

Title page of the printed record of the First Continental Congress.

*An East Prospect of the City of Philadelphia. Etching "Engrav'd
& Publish'd . . . by T. Jefferys, near Charing Cross," 1768.
LC-USZ62-3282*

To the King's Most Excellent Majesty.

Most Gracious Sovereign!

We your Majesty's faithful Subjects of the colonies of New-Hampshire, Massachusetts-Bay, Rhode-Island and Providence Plantations, Connecticut, New-York, New-Jersey, Pensylvania, the Counties of New-Castle, Kent and Sussex on Delaware, Maryland, Virginia, North-Carolina, and South-Carolina in behalf of ourselves and the inhabitants of those colonies who have deputed us to represent them in General Congress, by this our humble petition, beg leave to lay our grievances before the throne.

A standing army has been kept in these Colonies, ever since the conclusion of the late war, without the consent of our assemblies, and this army with a considerable naval armament has been employed to enforce the collection of taxes.

The Authority of the Commander in Chief, and, under him, of the Brigadiers General has in time of peace, been rendered supreme in all the civil governments in America.

The Commander in Chief of all your Majesty's forces in North-America has, in time of peace, been appointed Governor of a Colony.

The charges of usual offices have been greatly increased, and new, expensive and oppressive offices have been multiplied.

The judges of Admiralty and vice admiralty courts are impowered to receive their salaries and fees from the effects condemned by themselves. The officers of the customs are empowered to break open and enter houses without the authority of any civil Magistrate founded on legal information.

The

That your Majesty may enjoy every felicity through a long and glorious reign over loyal and happy subjects, and that your descendants may inherit your prosperity and dominions 'till time shall be no more, is and always will be our sincere and fervent prayer.

Philadelphia Octr 26. 1774

Henry Middleton, Presid.

from New Hampshire
John Sullivan
Nath. Folsom

From Massachusetts Bay
Thomas Cushing
Samuel Adams
John Adams
Rob. Treat Paine

From Rhode Island
Stephen Hopkins
Samuel Ward

From Pensylvania
E. Biddle
J. Galloway
John Dickinson
John Morton
Thomas Mifflin
George Ross
Charles Humphreys

From Delaware government
Caesar Rodney
Tho. M'Kean
George Read

From Connecticut
Elipht Dyer
Roger Sherman
Silas Deane

Philip Livingstone
John Alsop
Isaac Low
James Duane
John Jay
William Floyd
Henry Wisner
S. Boerum
} From New York

Will. Livingston
John De Hart
Stephen Crane
Richard Smith
} From New Jersey

George Read

Mat. Tilghman
Tho. Johnson, Jun
Will. Paca
Samuel Chase
} From Maryland

Rich. Henry Lee
Patrick Henry
Geo. Washington
Edmund Pendleton
Richard Bland
Benja. Harrison
} From Virginia

The first and last pages of the petition to George III from the First Continental Congress. This contemporary copy was evidently marked for the printer by Benjamin Franklin, who delivered the original petition in December 1774 to the Earl of Dartmouth, secretary of state for the colonies. From the Franklin papers.

In the spring of 1775 armed force was resorted to by Britons and Americans at four different places: Lexington and Concord, April 19, 1775; Williamsburg, Va., the next day; Fort Ticonderoga, N.Y., in early May; and Breed's Hill, near Bunker Hill, in Charlestown, Mass., in mid-June.

The battle of Lexington and Concord, the opening shot in the Revolutionary War, was a fight between British troops, attempting to capture colonial supplies, and Massachusetts minutemen, attempting to defend them. Forced to retreat to Boston, the British ran a gauntlet of American sniper fire, taking heavy casualties as they retired.

The Americans were less successful at Williamsburg, where they were unable to prevent the governor of Virginia, Lord Dunmore, from capturing the gunpowder stored there, but the successful attack on Fort Ticonderoga by a combined force under Ethan Allen and Benedict Arnold offset that reverse and put significant quantities of mortars and cannon into patriot hands. (The cannon, which were eventually positioned on Dorchester Heights overlooking Boston, enabled the patriots to force the British, on March 17, 1776, to evacuate the city.)

Patrick Henry. Lithograph by John T. Bowen, 1840, probably based on a painting by Thomas Sully. LC-USZ62-26672

Broadside announcement of the battles at Lexington and Concord, printed at Salem, Mass., by E. Russell and based on the account published in his Salem Gazette *on Friday, April 21, 1775. The broadside lists by name 40 colonials killed and 20 wounded in the battle. A broadside report of the British casualties in this encounter lists 65 dead, 180 wounded, and 27 missing.*

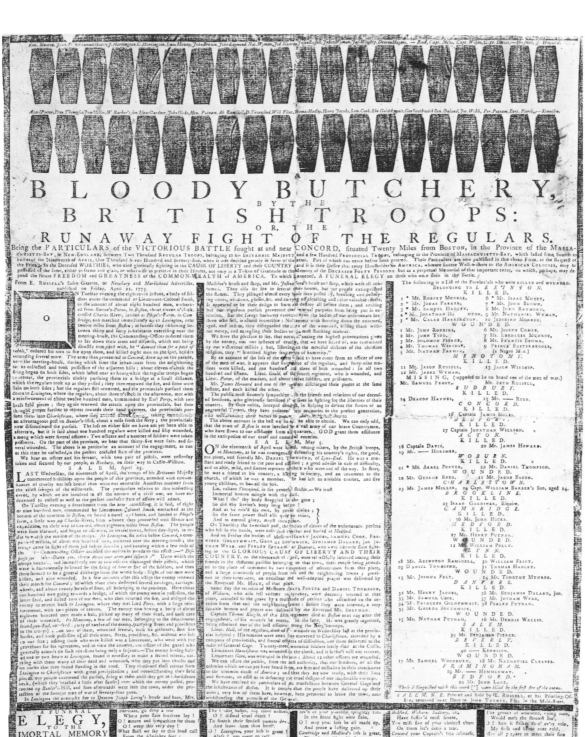

BLOODY BUTCHERY,
BY THE
BRITISH TROOPS:
OR, THE
RUNAWAY FIGHT OF THE REGULARS.

Being the PARTICULARS of the VICTORIOUS BATTLE fought at and near CONCORD, situated Twenty Miles from Boston, in the Province of the MASSACHUSETTS-BAY, in New-England, between Two Thousand Regular Troops, belonging to his Britannic Majesty, and a few Hundred Provincial Troops, belonging to the Province of Massachusetts-Bay, which lasted from Sunrise to Sunset, on the Nineteenth of April, One Thousand Seven Hundred and Seventy-five, when it was decided greatly in favor of the latter. Part of which has never before been printed. These Particulars are now published in this cheap Form, at the Request of the Friends to the Deceased WORTHIES, who died gloriously fighting in the CAUSE OF LIBERTY and their COUNTRY; and it is their Desire that every Householder in AMERICA, whoever desires Well-wishers to the AMERICAN COLONIES, may be possessed of the same, either to frame and glass, or otherwise to preserve in their Houses, not only as a Token of Gratitude to the Memory of the Deceased Forty Persons, but as a perpetual Memorial of that important event, on which, perhaps, may depend the future FREEDOM and GREATNESS of the COMMON-WEALTH of AMERICA. To which is annexed, A FUNERAL ELEGY on those who were slain in the Battle.

From E. RUSSELL's Salem Gazette, or Newbury and Marblehead Advertiser, published on Friday, April 21, 1775.

ON Tuesday evening the eighteenth instant, a body of soldiers under the command of Lieutenant-Colonel Smith, to the amount of about eight hundred men, embarked from Barton's-Point, in Boston, about eleven o'clock, crossed Charles-River, landed at Phip's-Farm, in Cambridge, and marched immediately up to Lexington, near twelve miles from Boston; at sunrise they observing between thirty and forty inhabitants exercising near the meeting-house, the Commanding-Officer ordered them to lay down their arms and disperse, which not being directly complied with, he "damned them for a pack of rebels," ordered his men to fire upon them, and killed eight men on the spot, besides wounding several more. The army then proceeded to Concord, drew up on the parade, near the meeting-house, during which time the inhabitants from the neighbouring towns collected and took possession of the adjacent hills; about eleven o'clock the firing began on both sides, which lasted near an hour, when the regular troops began to retreat, the provincials closely pursuing them to a bridge at a small distance, which the regulars took up as they pulled; they then renewed the fire, and some were slain on both sides; but the regulars still retreated, and the provincials pursued them down to Lexington, where the regulars, about three o'clock in the afternoon, met with a reinforcement of about twelve hundred men, commanded by Earl Percy, with two brass field pieces; they again renewed the attack upon the provincials, but soon thought proper further to retreat towards their head-quarters, the provincials pursued them into Charlestown, where they arrived about sun-set, taking immediately an advantageous post on Bunker's-Hill, about a mile from the ferry; the provincials now discontinued the pursuit. The loss on either side we have not yet been able to ascertain, but it is said about one hundred regulars were killed and fifty wounded, among which were several officers: Two officers and a number of soldiers were taken prisoners. On the part of the province, we hear that thirty-five were slain, and some wounded. The above is as particular an account of this engagement, as can at this time be collected, in the present confused state of the province.

We hear an officer and his servant, with two pair of pistols, were yesterday taken and secured by our people, at Roxbury, on their way to Castle-William.

SALEM, April 25.

LAST Wednesday, the nineteenth of April, the troops of his Britannic Majesty commenced hostilities upon the people of this province, attended with circumstances of cruelty not less brutal than what our venerable Ancestors received from the vilest savages of the wilderness. The particulars relative to this interesting event, by which we are involved in all the horrors of a civil war, we have endeavoured to collect as well as the present confused state of affairs will admit.

On Tuesday evening a detachment from the army consisting, it is said, of eight or nine hundred men, commanded by Lieutenant Colonel Smith, embarked at the bottom of the common in Boston, on board a number of boats, and landed at Phip's farm, a little way up Charles-River, from whence they proceeded with silence and expedition, on their way to Concord, about eighteen miles from Boston. The people were soon alarmed, and began to assemble, in several places, before day-light, in order to watch the motion of the troops. At Lexington, six miles below Concord, a company of militia, of about one hundred men, mustered near the meeting-house; the troops came in sight of them just before sunrise, and running within a few rods of them, the Commanding Officer accosted the militia in words to this effect:—"Disperse ye Rebels—Damn you, throw down your arms and disperse:" Upon which the troops huzza'd, and immediately one or two officers discharged their pistols, which were instantaneously followed by the firing of four or five of the soldiers, and then there seemed to be a general discharge from the whole body: Eight of our men were killed, and nine wounded. In a few minutes after this action the enemy renewed their march for Concord; at which place they destroyed several carriages, carriage-wheels, and about twenty barrels of flour, all belonging to the province. Here about one hundred men going towards a bridge, of which the enemy were in possession, the latter fired, and killed two of our men, who then returned the fire, and obliged the enemy to retreat back to Lexington, where they met Lord Percy, with a large reinforcement, with two pieces of cannon. The enemy having a body of about eighteen hundred men made a halt, picked up many of their dead, and took care of their wounded. At Menotomy, a few of our men, belonging to the detachment from Lynn-End, attacked a party of twelve of the enemy, (carrying stores and provisions to the troops) and two of them, wounded several, took six prisoners, four horses, and took possession of all their arms, stores, provisions, &c. without any loss on our side; among those who were killed was a Lieutenant, who went with the provisions for his recreation, and to view the country, one officer of the guard who casually attends on such occasions being only a serjeant.—The enemy having halted one or two hours at Lexington, found it necessary to make a second retreat, carrying with them many of their dead and wounded, who they put into chaises and on horses that they found standing in the road. They continued their retreat from Lexington to Charlestown with great precipitation; and notwithstanding their field pieces, our people continued the pursuit, firing at them until they got to Charlestown neck, (which they reached a little after sunset) over which the enemy passed, proceeded up Bunker's-Hill, and soon afterwards went into the town, under the protection of the Somerset man of war of seventy-four guns.

In Lexington the enemy set fire to Deacon Joseph Loring's house and barn, Mrs.

Mulliken's house and shop, and Mr. Joshua Bond's house and shop, which were all consumed. They also set fire to several other houses, but our people extinguished the flames. They pillaged almost every house they passed by, breaking and destroying doors, windows, glasses, &c. and carrying off clothing and other valuable effects. It appeared to be their design to burn and destroy all before them; and nothing but our vigorous pursuit prevented their infernal purposes from being put in execution. But the savage barbarity exercised upon the bodies of our unfortunate brethren who fell, is almost incredible: Not contented with shooting down the unarmed, aged, and infirm, they disregarded the cries of the wounded, killing them without mercy, and mangling their bodies in the most shocking manner.

We have the pleasure to say, that notwithstanding the highest provocations given by the enemy, not one instance of cruelty, that we have heard of, was committed by our victorious militia; but, listening to the merciful dictates of the christian religion, they "breathed higher sentiments of humanity."

By an account of the loss of the enemy said to have come from an officer of one of the men of war, it appears that sixty-three of the regulars, and forty-nine marines were killed, and one hundred and three of both wounded: In all two hundred and fifteen. Lieut. Gould, of the fourth regiment, who is wounded, and Lieut. Potter, of the marines, and about twelve soldiers, are prisoners.

Mr. James Howard and one of the regulars discharged their pieces at the same instant, and each killed the other.

The public most sincerely sympathize with the friends and relations of our deceased brethren, who gloriously sacrificed their lives in fighting for the liberties of their country. By their noble, intrepid conduct, in helping to defeat the forces of an ungrateful Tyrant, they have endeared their memories to the present generation, who will transmit their names to posterity with the greatest honour.

The above account is the best we have been able to obtain. We can only add, that the town of Boston is now invested by a vast army of our brave Countrymen, who have flown to our assistance from all quarters. GOD grant them assistance in the extirpation of our cruel and unnatural enemies.

SALEM, May 5.

ON the nineteenth of April were slain, among others, by the British troops, at Menotomy, as he was courageously defending his country's rights, the good, the pious, and friendly Mr. Daniel Townsend, of Lynn-End. He was a constant and ready friend to the poor and afflicted; a good adviser in case of difficulty, and an able, mild, and sincere reprover of those who were out of the way. In short, he was a friend to his country, a blessing to society, and an ornament to the church, of which he was a member. He has left an amiable consort, and five young children, to bemoan the loss.

Let, valiant Townsend, in the peaceful shades.—We trust
Immortal honors mingle with thy dust.
What I tho' thy body struggled in the gore;
So did thy Savior's body long before !
And as he rais'd his own, by power divine;
So the same power shall also quick'n thine,
And in eternal glory, mayst thou shine.

On Thursday the twentieth past, the bodies of eleven of the unfortunate persons who fell in the battle, were collected together and buried at Medford.

And on Friday the bodies of Messieurs Henry Jacobs, Samuel Cook, Ebenezer Goldthwait, George Southwick, Benjamin Daland, jun. Jotham Webb, and Perley Putnam, of Danvers, who were likewise slain fighting in the GLORIOUS CAUSE OF LIBERTY AND THEIR COUNTRY, on the nineteenth of April, were respectfully interred among their friends in the different parishes belonging to that town, their corpse being attended to the place of interment by two companies of minute-men from this place, and a large concourse of people from this and the neighboring towns; previous to their interment, an excellent and well-adapted prayer was delivered by the Reverend Mr. Holt, of that place.

Some day the relations of Messieurs Asafel Porter and Daniel Thompson, of Woburn, who also fell victims to tyranny, were decently interred at that place, attended to the grave by a multitude of persons who assembled on the occasion from that and the neighboring towns: Before they were interred, a very suitable sermon and prayer was delivered by the Reverend Mr. Sherman.

Captain Thomas Knight, of the fifth regiment died at Boston last day after the engagement, of his wounds he received in the same. It was greatly regretted, being esteemed one of the best officers among the King's troops.

Lieut. Hull, of the regulars, died of the wounds on Wednesday last at the provincial hospital: His remains were next day conveyed to Charlestown, attended by a company of provincials, and several officers of distinction, and there delivered to the order of General Gage. Twenty-three wounded soldiers lately died at the Castle.

Lieutenant Hawkshaw was wounded in the cheek, and it is tho't will not recover. Lieutenant Gore, was wounded in the arm; about 12 other officers are wounded.

We can assure the public, from the best authority, that our brethren, or all the colonies which we can yet have heard from, are firm and unshaken in this attachment to the common cause of America; and that they are now ready, with their lives and fortunes, to assist us in defeating the cruel designs of our implacable enemies.

We have received no particulars of the transactions between General Gage and the inhabitants of Boston. It is certain that the people have delivered up their arms; very few of them have, however, been permitted to leave the town, notwithstanding the promise of the General.

The following is a List of the Provincials who were KILLED and WOUNDED.

BELONGING TO LEXINGTON.
KILLED.

1 * Mr. Robert Monroe, 6 Mr. Isaac Muzzy,
2 * Mr. Jonas Parker, 7 * Mr. John Brown,
3 * Mr. Samuel Hadley, 8 Mr. John Raymond,
4 * Mr. Jonathan Harrington, 9 Mr. Nathaniel Wyman,
5 * Mr. Caleb Harrington, 10 Jedidiah Monroe,

WOUNDED.

1 Mr. John Robbins, 6 Mr. Joseph Comee,
2 Mr. John Tidd, 7 Mr. Ebenezer Munroe,
3 Mr. Solomon Pierce, 8 Mr. Francis Brown,
4 Mr. Thomas Winship, 9 Prince Easterbrooks,
5 Mr. Nathan Farmer, (a Negro Man.)

MENOTOMY.
KILLED.

11 Mr. Jason Russell, 13 Jason Winship,
12 Mr. Jabez Wyman,

MISSING, (supposed to be on board one of the men of war.)
Mr. Samuel Frost, Mr. Seth Russell,

SUDBURY.
KILLED.

14 Deacon Haynes, 15 Mr. —— Reed.

CONCORD.
KILLED.

16 Captain James Miles,

SUDBURY.
KILLED.

17 Captain Jonathan Willson,

ACTON.
KILLED.

18 Captain Davis, 20 Mr. James Howard.
19 Mr. —— Hosmer,

WOBURN.
KILLED.

21 * Mr. Asael Porter, 22 Mr. Daniel Thompson.
10 Mr. George Reed, 11 Mr. Jacob Bacon.

CHARLESTOWN.
KILLED.

23 Mr. James Miller, 24 Capt. William Barber's Son, aged 14.

BROOKLINE.
KILLED.

25 Isaac Gardiner, Esquire.

CAMBRIDGE.
KILLED.

26 Mr. John Hicks,

MEDFORD.
KILLED.

27 Mr. Henry Putnam,

WOUNDED.

12 Mr. William Polly.

LYNN.
KILLED.

28 Mr. Abednego Ramsdell, 30 William Flint,
29 Daniel Townsend, 31 Thomas Hadley.

WOUNDED.

13 Mr. Joshua Felt, 14 Mr. Timothy Munroe.

DANVERS.
KILLED.

32 Mr. Henry Jacobs, 36 Mr. Benjamin Daland, jun.
33 Mr. Samuel Cook, 37 Mr. Jotham Webb,
34 Mr. Ebenezer Goldthwait, 38 Perley Putnam.
35 Mr. George Southwick,

WOUNDED.

15 Mr. Nathan Putnam, 16 Mr. Dennis Wallis.

SALEM.
KILLED.

39 Mr. Benjamin Pierce,

BEVERLY.
KILLED.

40 —— Kennison.

WOUNDED.

17 Mr. Samuel Woodbury, 18 Mr. Nathaniel Cleaves.

FRAMINGHAM.
19 Mr. —— Hemmenway.

BEDFORD.
20 Mr. John Lane.

Those * distinguished with this mark [*] were killed by the first fire of the enemy.

SALEM, N. E. Printed and Sold by E. RUSSELL, at his Printing-Office, removed next Door to John Turner, Esq; in the Main-Street.

A FUNERAL ELEGY, TO THE IMMORTAL MEMORY

Of those Worthies, who were slain in the Battle of Concord, April 19, 1775.

AID me ye nine ! my muse assist,
  A sad tale to relate,
When such a number of brave men
  Met their unhappy fate.
At Lexington they met their foe
  Completely all equip'd,
Their guns and swords made glitt'ring show ;
  But their base scheme was nipp'd.

Americans, go drop a tear
  Where your slain brethren lay !
O ! mourn and sympathize for them
  O ! weep this very day !
What shall we say to this loud call
  From the Almighty sent ;
It surely bids both great and small
  Seek God's face and repent.
Words can't express the ghastly scene
  That here presents to view,
When forty our brave Countrymen
  Sure bid their friends adieu.
To think how awful it must seem,
  To hear widows relent
Their husbands and their children
  Who to the grave were sent.

Seiz'd with your youthful springing time,
  In the fierce fight were slain,
O ! may you; loss be all made up,
  And prove a lasting gain.
Cambridge and Medford's loss is great,
  Though not like Acton's town,
Where three fierce military sons
  Met their untimely doom.
Menotomy and Charlestown met
  A sore and heavy stroke,
In losing five your brave townsmen
  Who fell by tyrant's yoke.
Let's not forget the Danvers race,
  So late in battle slain,
Their courage and their valor show,
  Upon the crimson'd plain.

In Bedford, Woburn, Sudbury, all,
  Have suffer'd most severe,
You miss five of your choicest ones
  On them isn't drop a tear.
Concord your Captain's loss rehearse,
  His loss is felt severe,
Come, brethren, join with me in verse,
  His mem'ry hence revere.
O 'Squire Gardiner's death we feel,
  And sympathizing mourn,
Let's drop a tear when it we tell,
  And view his hapless urn.
We sore regret poor Pierce's death,
  A stroke to Salem's town,
Where tears did flow from ev'ry brow,
  When the sad tidings come.

The groans of wounded, dying men,
  Would melt the stoutest soul,
O ! how it strikes tho' ev'ry vein,
  My flesh and blood runs cold.
We all prepare to meet their fate
  At God's tribunal bar,
And may each terrible alarm
  For death so awe prepare.
You Country calls you far and near,
  America's sons awake,
Your helmet, buckler, and your spear,
  The Lord's own arm now take.
His shield will keep us from all harm,
  Tho' thousands 'gainst us rise,
His buckler we must sure put on,
  If we would win the prize.

Joseph Warren, a prominent Boston physician and the successor to John Hancock as president of the Massachusetts Provincial Congress. Joining the action at Charlestown on June 17, 1775, the 34-year-old Warren was one of the few Americans to be killed in the redoubt on Breed's Hill. Engraving by John Norman in *An Impartial History of the War in America (Boston, 1781)*. LC-USZ62-27694

In *Provincial Congress,*

Cambridge, February 14, 1775.

WHEREAS it appears neceffary for the Defence of the Lives, Liberties, and Properties, of the Inhabitants of this Province, that this Congrefs on the firft Day of their next Seffion, fhould be made fully acquainted with the Number and Military Equipments of the Militia, and Minute Men in this Province ; and alfo the Town Stock of Ammunition in each Town and Diftrict :

It is therefore RESOLVED, That it be and it is hereby recommended, to the commanding Officers of each Regiment of Minute Men, that now is or fhall be formed in this Province, that they review the feveral Companies in their refpective Regiments, or caufe them to be reviewed, and take an exact State of their Numbers, and Equipment, —and where there is any Company that is not incorporated into a Regiment, the commanding Officer thereof fhall review the feveral Companies, or caufe them to be reviewed, and take a like State of their Numbers and Equipment.—And it is alfo recommended to the Colonels or commanding Officers of each Regiment of Militia in this Province, that they review the feveral Companies in their refpective Regiments, or caufe them to be reviewed, and take a State of their Numbers and Accoutrements ; which faid State of the Minute Men and Militia, fhall be by faid Officers returned in Writing to this Congrefs, on the firft Day of their Seffion after the Adjournment.——

And it is further RESOLVED, That it be recommended to the Select-Men of each Town and Diftrict in the Province, that on the fame Day they make return in Writing of the State of the Town and Diftrict Stock of Ammunition, and War-like Stores to this Congrefs.

Signed by Order of the Provincial Congrefs,

JOHN HANCOCK, Prefident.

A true Extract from the Minutes,

BENJAMIN LINCOLN, Secretary.

During the night of June 16, 1775, the patriots sent a detachment of the troops who were besieging Boston to occupy the high ground on the Charlestown peninsula, where, just east of Bunker Hill, they built a redoubt. The next morning they reinforced it. In the afternoon British troops attacked, moving directly up the hill in the face of enemy gunfire. Twice they came forward and were driven back. On their third assault, they dislodged the patriots and won control of the peninsula. With King Pyrrhus, however, the British could have exclaimed that another such victory would ruin them, for they suffered more than 1,150 casualties, while American losses were fewer than 450.

With the Battle of Bunker Hill, the first phase of the conflict came to an end. Eyes turned to Philadelphia, where the Congress had reconvened, now to lead a country in armed rebellion.

A resolution by the illegally organized Congress of Massachusetts Bay, asking for information about "the Number and Military Equipments of the Militia, and Minute Men in this Province."

Thomas Gage, commander in chief of British forces in North America and governor of Massachusetts Bay Province. His limitations as a military strategist exposed by the Battle of Bunker Hill, Gage was recalled to England in October 1775. Engraving in The Town and Country Magazine (May 1781). LC-USZ62-45419

Rough draft, in water color, of the Battle of Bunker Hill, drawn shortly after the battle by Lieut. Thomas Page, Gen. William Howe's aide-de-camp. From the Faden Collection.

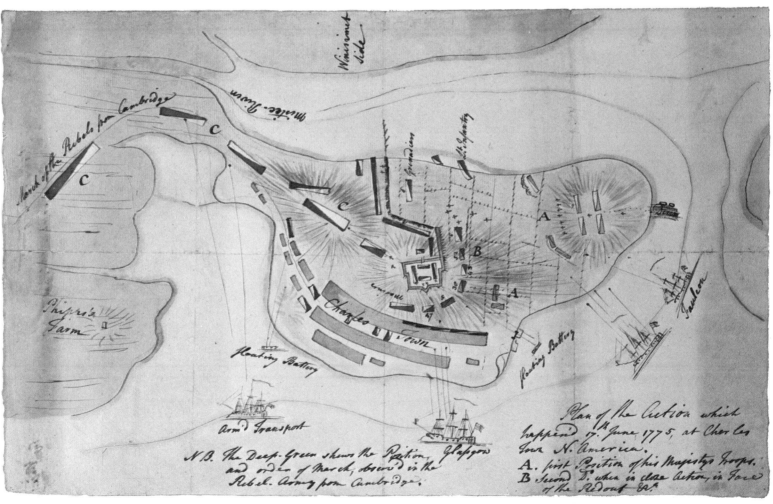

When the Second Continental Congress met at the state-house in Philadelphia on May 10, 1775, its members had no idea that they would be sitting as a continuous body for the next 14 years. When they finished their work a war had been won, independence had been attained, and a new nation had been established.

Congress Prosecutes the War

Most of the delegates who gathered in Philadelphia in the spring of 1775 were veterans of the first Congress. Among the newcomers was Benjamin Franklin, recently returned from England. The Adamses brought John Hancock, and New Jersey sent John Witherspoon, the president of the college at Princeton. Peyton Randolph of Virginia, who presided over Congress, returned to Virginia after a few weeks, and a substitute named Thomas Jefferson took his place. With the arrival in autumn of Lyman Hall of Georgia, all 13 colonies were represented in the Congress for the first time.

An engraving by James Trenchard after a drawing by Charles Willson Peale of what has come to be known as Independence Hall. LC-USZ62-9486

*George Washington's commission from the Continental Congress
as "Commander in Chief of the army of the United Colonies and
of all the forces raised or to be raised by them and of all others
who shall voluntarily offer their service and join the said army."
From the Washington papers.*

The war demanded Congress' immediate attention. The New England militia, assembled around Boston, needed organization and supplies. In a moment of inspiration, the Congress appointed one of its own members, Col. George Washington of Virginia, to command the American land forces. To obtain regional balance, Artemas Ward of Massachusetts was appointed second in command. An eccentric former British officer, Charles Lee, was named third in command. Washington's appointment gave universal satisfaction, and his arrival at American headquarters in Cambridge marked the beginning of the transformation of a collection of volunteers into a regular army.

By the summer of 1775 most of the delegates were pessimistic about the chances of peacefully accommodating the dispute with Great Britain, yet no one would publicly declare for independence. Most hoped against hope that some way could be found to settle the conflict which would leave them with autonomy within the British Empire. The ambivalent mood of the delegates was reflected in two actions, taken only a day apart. On the one hand they issued a manifesto, drafted in part by Jefferson and entitled "A Declaration of the Causes and Necessity of Taking Up Arms," in which a willingness to fight "for the preservation of our liberties" was emphatically proclaimed. Almost simultaneously they followed the suggestion of John Dickinson and dispatched to the king an "Olive Branch Petition," respectfully requesting a resolution of the difficulties.

To the Kings most excellent Majesty

Most gracious Sovereign

We your Majesty's faithful subjects of the colonies of New hampshire, Massachusetts-bay, Rhode island and Providence plantations, Connecticut, New-York, New-Jersey, Pennsylvania, the counties of New Castle Kent and Sussex on Delaware, Maryland, Virginia, North Carolina and South Carolina, in behalf of ourselves and the inhabitants of these colonies, who have deputed us to represent them in general Congress, entreat your Majesty's gracious attention to this our humble petition.

The union between our Mother country and these colonies, and the energy of mild and just government, produced benefits so remarkably important, and afforded such an assurance of their permanency and increase, that the wonder & envy of other nations were excited, while they beheld Great Britain rising to a power the most extraordinary the world had ever known.

Her rivals observing, that there was no probability of this happy connection being broken by civil dissentions, and apprehending its future effects, if left any longer undisturbed, resolved to prevent her receiving such continual and formidable accessions of wealth and strength, by checking the growth of these settlements from which they were to be derived —

In the prosecution of this attempt events so unfavourable to the design took place, that every friend to the interests of Great Britain and these colonies entertained

pleasing

Battle Scenes:
October 1775–June 1776

Except for the invasion of Quebec via New York and Maine, operations after Bunker Hill and before the Declaration of Independence were waged along coastal areas from Maine to South Carolina. These alternately encouraged both sides.

Throughout the Revolution many Americans believed that Canada might join the patriot cause. By mid-September 1775 a two-pronged attack was directed against the British stronghold at Quebec, but it failed when on the last day of the year Richard Montgomery was killed and Benedict Arnold badly wounded leading a futile assault on the city in a blinding snowstorm.

Benedict Arnold. Mezzotint engraving by Johann Martin Will, published in London in 1776. LC-USZ62-39570

Sir Guy Carleton, governor of Quebec and commander of the British forces in Canada, 1767–78, succeeded Sir Henry Clinton as commander in chief in America, 1782–83. Engraving in The Westminster Magazine *(October 1783). LC-USZ62-7845*

By his Excellency the Right Honourable JOHN Earl of DUNMORE, his Majesty's Lieutenant and Governour-General of the Colony and Dominion of Virginia, and Vice-Admiral of the same:

A PROCLAMATION.

AS I have ever entertained Hopes that an Accommodation might have taken Place between *Great Britain* and this Colony, without being compelled, by my Duty, to this most disagreeable, but now absolutely necessary Step, rendered so by a Body of armed Men, unlawfully assembled, firing on his Majesty's Tenders, and the Formation of an Army, and that Army now on their March to attack his Majesty's Troops, and destroy the well-disposed Subjects of this Colony: To defeat such treasonable Purposes, and that all such Traitors, and their Abetters, may be brought to Justice, and that the Peace and good Order of this Colony may be again restored, which the ordinary Course of the civil Law is unable to effect, I have thought fit to issue this my Proclamation, hereby declaring, that until the aforesaid good Purposes can be obtained, I do, in Virtue of the Power and Authority to me given, by his Majesty, determine to execute martial Law, and cause the same to be executed throughout this Colony; and to the End that Peace and good Order may the sooner be restored, I do require every Person capable of bearing Arms to resort to his Majesty's S T A N-DARD, or be looked upon as Traitors to his Majesty's Crown and Government, and thereby become liable to the Penalty the Law inflicts upon such Offences, such as Forfeiture of Life, Confiscation of Lands, &c. &c. And I do hereby farther declare all indented Servants, Negroes, or others (appertaining to Rebels) free, that are able and willing to bear Arms, they joining his Majesty's Troops, as soon as may be, for the more speedily reducing this Colony to a proper Sense of their Duty, to his Majesty's Crown and Dignity. I do farther order, and require, all his Majesty's liege Subjects to retain their Quitrents, or any other Taxes due, or that may become due, in their own Custody, till such Time as Peace may be again restored to this at present most unhappy Country, or demanded of them for their former salutary Purposes, by Officers properly authorised to receive the same.

GIVEN under my Hand, on Board the Ship **William**, off Norfolk, the 7th Day of **November**, *in the 16th Year of his Majesty's Reign.*

D U N M O R E.

G O D SAVE THE K I N G.

While the Canadian invasion was in progress, a British fleet off the Maine coast bombarded Falmouth (later Portland), destroying a majority of the more than 200 houses there. Several weeks later, Virginia's Governor Dunmore celebrated New Year's Day, 1776, by ordering artillery fire into the houses of Norfolk patriots, who in revenge burned the homes of their loyalist neighbors.

American fortunes improved as the winter of 1776 gave way to spring, for the patriots successively routed loyalists at Moores Creek Bridge in North Carolina (February 27, 1776), compelled the British army of occupation to evacuate Boston (March 17, 1776), and repelled a naval attack against Charleston (June 28, 1776). These successes helped to inspire the delegates to the Continental Congress with the courage to sever the ties with the mother country.

Declaration of martial law and an offer of emancipation to those in servitude who would rally to the king's standard, by the royal governor of Virginia. Threats on his life had induced Lord Dunmore, in June 1775, to move the seat of government from Williamsburg to a British warship.

Henry Knox, chief of artillery in the Continental army. His success in transporting captured cannon and mortars overland from Fort Ticonderoga to Boston in the winter of 1775–76 was a major factor in compelling the British to evacuate that city. Engraving by John Norman, in An Impartial History of the War in America *(Boston, 1782). LC-USZ62-45244*

This contemporary German woodcut is titled "Correct depiction of the capitol and fortress Boston in America which was besieged and reconquered by the American provincials in the month of March 1776." Shown are a prospect of the city, its bombardment by American cannon, and its evacuation by British troops and colonial loyalists. LC-USZ62-45548

SIR HENRY CLINTON

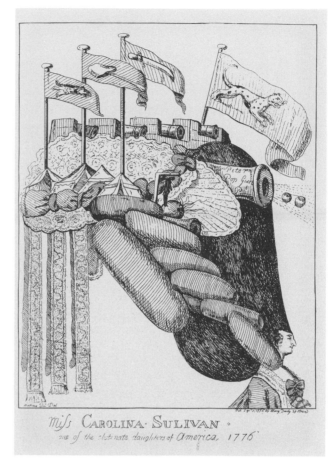

Miſs CAROLINA SULIVAN.
one of the obstinate daughters of America. 1776.

A British cartoon satirizing the defeat of British forces under the command of Commodore Peter Parker and Gen. Henry Clinton following their attack in June 1776 against Fort Sullivan (later Fort Moultrie), the guardian of the harbor at Charleston, S.C. LC-USZ62-46309

Second in command of British forces in America to Gen. William Howe, Clinton led an unsuccessful combined land-sea attack on Charleston, S.C., in June 1776. As successor to Howe, he was commander in chief of the British army in America from 1778 to 1782. Engraving in William Russell, The History of America from Its Discovery by Columbus to the Conclusion of the Late War (London, 1778). LC-USZ62-45262

The Declaration of Independence and The Beginnings of a New Government

George III refused even to receive the "Olive Branch Petition." Instead, he proclaimed the colonies in rebellion and ordered his military commanders to bring them to heel. Cast out of the king's protection and confronted with the efforts of his armies to subjugate them, the Americans perceived the absurdity of continuing to acknowledge allegiance to the British Crown. Independence now appeared to the majority of delegates in Congress to be the only means of national salvation. Still, there were many waiverers, and without the assistance of Thomas Paine, the immigrant son of a British corsetmaker, independence would have had a laborious passage. On January 9, 1776, Philadelphia and, quickly afterward, the entire continent was electrified by the appearance of Paine's *Common Sense*, the most famous pamphlet in American history. Deriding George III—the "Royal Brute of Britain"—and demolishing the objections to independence, Paine rallied public opinion behind it.

On July 2, 1776, Congress passed a resolution proclaiming America independent. The resolution had been introduced by Richard Henry Lee of Virginia on June 7, 1776, in the following words: "these United Colonies are, and of right ought to be, free and independent States. . . . all political connection between them and the State of Great Britain is, and of right ought to be, totally dissolved." A committee consisting of John Adams, Benjamin Franklin,

Tom Paine, author of Common Sense, *in his mid-50's. Engraving by William Sharp, 1793, after a painting a year earlier by George Romney. LC-USZ62-8238*

The response of the Crown to the Olive Branch Petition.

32

By his EXCELLENCY

WILLIAM TRYON, Esquire,

Captain General, and Governor in Chief in and over the Province of *New-York*, and the Territories depending thereon in *America*, Chancellor and Vice Admiral of the fame.

A PROCLAMATION.

WHEREAS I have received His Majefty's Royal Proclamation, given at the Court at *St. James's*, the Twenty-third Day of *Auguft* laft, in the Words following:

BY THE KING,

A · Proclamation,

For fuppreffing REBELLION and SEDITION.

GEORGE R.

WHEREAS many of our Subjects in divers Parts of our Colonies and Plantations in *North-America*, misled by dangerous and ill defigning Men, and forgetting the Allegiance which they owe to the Power that has protected and fustained them, after various disorderly Acts committed in difturbance of the public Peace, to the Obstruction of lawful Commerce, and to the Oppreffion of our loyal Subjects carrying on the fame, have at length proceeded to an open and avowed Rebellion, by arraying themfelves in hoftile Manner, to withftand the Execution of the Law, and traitoroufly preparing, ordering and levying War againft us: And whereas there is Reafon to apprehend that fuch Rebellion hath been much promoted and encouraged by the traitorous Correfpondence, Counfels, and Comfort of divers wicked and defperate Perfons within this Realm:---To the End therefore that none of our Subjects may neglect or violate their Duty through Ignorance thereof, or through any Doubt of the Protection which the Law will afford to their Loyalty and Zeal; have thought fit, by and with the Advice of our Privy Council, to iffue this our Royal Proclamation, hereby declaring, that not only all our Officers civil and Military, are obliged to exert their utmoft Endeavours to fuppref fuch Rebellion, and to bring the Traitors to Juftice; but that all our Subjects of this Realm and the Dominions thereunto belonging, are bound by Law to be aiding and affifting in the Suppreffion of fuch Rebellion, and to difclofe and make known all traitorous Confpiracies and Attempts againft us, our Crown and Dignity: And we do accordingly ftrictly charge and command all our Officers, as well Civil as Military, and all other our obedient and loyal Subjects, to ufe their utmoft Endeavours to withftand and fuppref fuch Rebellion, and to difclofe and make known all Treafons and traitorous Confpiracies which they fhall know to be againft us, our Crown and Dignity; and for that Purpofe, that they tranfmit to one of our principal Secretaries of State, or other proper Officer, due and full Information of all Perfons who fhall be found carrying on Correfpondence with, or in any Manner or Degree aiding or abetting the Perfons now in open Arms and Rebellion againft our Government within any of our Colonies and Plantations in *North-America*, in order to bring to condign Punifhment the Authors, Perpetrators, and Abettors of fuch traitorous Defigns.

Given at our Court at St. James's the Twenty-third Day of Auguft, *One Thoufand Seven Hundred and Seventy-five, in the Fifteenth Year of our Reign.*

In Obedience therefore to his Majefty's Commands to me given, I do hereby publifh and make known his Majefty's moft gracious Proclamation above recited; earneftly exhorting and requiring all his Majefty's loyal and faithful Subjects within this Province, as they value their Allegiance due to the beft of Sovereigns, their Dependance on and Protection from their Parent State, and the Bleffings of a mild, free, and happy Conftitution; and as they would fhun the fatal Calamities which are the inevitable Confequences of Sedition and Rebellion, to pay all due Obedience to the Laws of their Country, ferioufly to attend to his Majefty's faid Proclamation, and govern themfelves accordingly.

Given under my Hand and Seal at Arms, in the City of New-York, *the Fourteenth Day of* November, *One Thoufand Seven Hundred and Seventy-five, in the Sixteenth Year of the Reign of our Sovereign Lord* GEORGE *the Third, by the Grace of God of* Great-Britain, France *and* Ireland, *King, Defender of the Faith, and fo forth.*

WM. TRYON.

By his Excellency's Command,

SAMUEL BAYARD, Jun. D. Secry.

GOD SAVE THE *KING.*

A Declaration by the Representatives of the UNITED STATES OF AMERICA, in General Congress assembled.

When in the course of human events it becomes necessary for ~~a~~ one people to dissolve the political bands which have connected them with another, and to ~~[struck out]~~, as-sume among the powers of the earth the separate and equal ~~[struck out]~~ station to which the laws of nature & of nature's god entitle them, a decent respect to the opinions of mankind requires that they should declare the causes which impel them to the ~~[struck out]~~ separation.

We hold these truths to be self-evident; ~~sacred & undeniable~~ that all men are created equal ~~& independent~~, that ~~from that equal creation they derive~~ they are endowed by their creator with ~~[struck out]~~ ~~[struck out]~~ inherent & inalienable rights; that among ~~which~~ these are ~~[struck out]~~ life, liberty, & the pursuit of happiness; that to secure these ~~ends~~ rights, go-vernments are instituted among men, deriving their just powers from the consent of the governed; that whenever any form of government ~~shall~~ becomes destructive of these ends, it is the right of the people to alter or to abolish it, & to institute new government, laying it's foundation on such principles & organising it's powers in such form, as to them shall seem most likely to effect their safety & happiness. prudence indeed will dictate that governments long established should not be changed for light & transient causes: and accordingly all experience hath shewn that mankind are more disposed to suffer while evils are sufferable, than to right themselves by abolishing the forms to which they are accustomed. but when a long train of abuses & usurpations [begun at a distinguished period, &] pursuing invariably the same object, evinces a design to ~~subject~~ reduce them + under absolute Despotism, it is their right, it is their duty, to throw off such ~~government~~ + & to provide new guards for their future security. such has been the patient sufferance of these colonies; & such is now the necessity which constrains them to ~~expunge~~ alter their former systems of government. the history of the present ~~king of Great Britain~~ is a history of ~~unremitting~~ repeated injuries and usurpations, [among which appears no solitary fact ~~[struck out]~~ to contra-dict the uniform tenor of the rest,] all of which ~~but all~~ have in direct object the establishment of an absolute tyranny over these states. to prove this, let facts be submitted to a candid world, [for the truth of which we pledge a faith yet unsullied by falsehood.]

Thomas Jefferson, Robert R. Livingston, and Roger Sherman was appointed to prepare a statement on the subject of Lee's resolution. Because Jefferson's writings were characterized by "a peculiar felicity of expression," as Adams put it, the Virginian was asked to prepare the draft. Although both the committee and Congress made changes, the statement remained distinctly Jeffersonian.

The delegates approved the document on July 4, 1776, voted on the 19th to engross it, and signed it on August 2. Its purpose was not to declare independence—that had been done on July 2—but to explain to the world the reasons for the American action. The words in which it did so have become immortal.

Thomas Jefferson's rough draft of the Declaration of Independence. LC-USP6-187A-191A

Richard Henry Lee, prominent member of a well-known Virginia family and an early supporter of the movement toward independence. Lee served as president of Congress in 1784. Engraving by Peter Maverick and James B. Longacre, in John Sanderson, Biography of the Signers of the Declaration of Independence *(Philadelphia, 1820–27). LC-USZ62-7680*

Thomas Jefferson, who, along with John Adams, died on the 50th anniversary of the Declaration of Independence, asked to be remembered for three things: the Declaration of Independence, the Virginia statute for religious freedom, and the University of Virginia. Engraving by Cornelius Tiebout, 1801, after a painting in 1800 by Rembrandt Peale. LC-USZ62-7583

Establishing a new government for the new nation was a vexing problem. A tentative start had been made as early as July 1775, when Benjamin Franklin proposed that the embattled colonies join in a confederation. In June 1776 a committee led by John Dickinson began to draft Articles of Confederation, which were debated intermittently throughout that year and into the next. In November 1777 a draft was finally approved and sent to the states, but since the Articles required unanimous approval, ratification was delayed until 1781. Government under the Articles became operative on March 1, 1781, but the inherent defects of the Articles limited the government's effectiveness and ensured it a short life. The central government acquired authority, although not real power, in several areas and was greatly hindered by the absence of the power to tax. The most important accomplishment while the Articles were in effect was the establishment of a system of government and land disposal for the Northwest Territory, which guaranteed an orderly transition from territorial status to statehood.

A balance sheet on the Articles of Confederation is difficult to draw. The harsh assessment of 19th-century historians that the Articles left Americans "a people without a government" has been modified by the research of 20th-century historians, some of whom find much to admire in the Articles. At a minimum, most will agree that the Articles preserved the union while a consensus developed that a new, stronger system of government was needed.

John Hancock, a Boston merchant who signed the Declaration of Independence in his capacity as president of the Continental Congress. Engraving by John Norman in An Impartial History of the War in America *(Boston, 1781). LC-USZ62-45235*

First page of Benjamin Franklin's plan of confederation, 1775, in the hand of and annotated by Thomas Jefferson. From the Jefferson papers.

On November 15, 1777, Congress agreed to the Articles of Confederation, and a printing of 300 copies was ordered. On November 28 the printed copies were delivered to Congress, then meeting in York, Pa., after having convened for one day at Lancaster, Pa., following its removal from Philadelphia late in September in the face of the advancing British army. Shown here is the title page of one of the official copies, inscribed on the last page "By Order of Congress Henry Laurens President."

Articles of confederation and perpetual Union propos'd by the delegates of the
several colonies of New Hampshire &c in General Congress met at Philadelphia
May. 10. 1775.

Art. I.   The name of this confederacy shall henceforth be "The united States of
North America"

Art. II.   The said united colonies hereby severally enter into a firm league of frien
-dship with each other, binding on themselves & their posterity, for their common
defence against their enemies, for the security of their liberties & properties, the
safety of their persons & families & their mutual & general welfare.

Art. III.   That each colony shall enjoy & retain as much as it may think fit of its own
present laws, customs, rights, privileges & peculiar jurisdiction within it's own
limits; and may amend it's own constitution as shall seem best to it's own
assembly or convention.

Art. IV.   That for the more convenient management of general interests, delegates
shall be annually elected in each colony to meet in General Congress at such time
& place as shall be agreed on in the next preceding Congress. only where practical
circumstances do not make a deviation necessary, it is understood to be a rule
that each succeeding Congress be held in a different colony till the whole number
be gone through & so in perpetual rotation; & that accordingly the next Con
-gress after the present shall be held at Annapolis in Maryland.

Art. V.   That the power & duty of the Congress shall extend to the determining on war
& peace, the entering into alliances, the reconciliation with Great Britain, the
settling all disputes & differences between colony & colony if such should arise; &
the planting of new colonies when proper. the Congress shall also make such
general ordinances as tho' necessary to the general welfare, particular assemblies cannot be competent to, viz. those that may relate to our general commerce, or general currency; to the establishment of posts, the regulation of our
common forces, the Congress shall also have the appointment of all officers,
civil & military, appertaining to the general confederacy, such as general
treasurer, secretary &c.

Art. VI.   All charges of wars & all other general expenses to be incurred for the
common welfare, shall be defrayed out of a common treasury, which is to be
supplied by each colony in proportion to it's number of male polls between the
16 & 60 years of age; the taxes for paying that proportion are to be laid &
levied by the laws of each colony.

Art. VII.   The number of Delegates to be elected & sent to the Congress by each colony
shall be regulated from time to time by the number of such polls returned;
so as that one Delegate be allowed for every 5000 polls & the delegates are
bring with them to every Congress, an authenticated return of the number of po
in their respective provinces which is to be triennially taken for the purposes a
forementioned.

ARTICLES

OF

Confederation

AND

Perpetual Union

BETWEEN THE

STATES

OF

NEW-HAMPSHIRE, MASSACHUSETTS-BAY, RHODE-
ISLAND AND PROVIDENCE PLANTATIONS, CON-
NECTICUT, NEW-YORK, NEW-JERSEY, PENNSYL-
VANIA, DELAWARE, MARYLAND, VIRGINIA,
NORTH-CAROLINA, SOUTH-CAROLINA AND GEOR-
GIA.

LANCASTER:
PRINTED BY FRANCIS BAILEY.
M,DCC,LXXVII.

This hand-colored etching shows the arrival of British troops in New York City following its abandonment in mid-September 1776 by the American forces commanded by General Washington. LC-USZ62-26673

The War Continues:

August 1776–October 1780

By late summer the tempo of the 1776 campaign had quickened, and the British and American armies were poised for a confrontation. They first met on Long Island, from where a well-organized retreat across the East River was conducted by the Americans in late August, before a serious engagement for control of Manhattan Island in mid-September. Washington subsequently fell back to Westchester County, where an indecisive battle was fought at White Plains in October. Turning southwestward, the British moved against Fort Washington on the Hudson and captured it and its garrison in mid-November, dealing the Americans one of the greatest single losses suffered during the entire war.

Washington's army, dispirited after the loss of the Hudson River fort, retreated across New Jersey to Trenton, escaping defeat there only by crossing the Delaware into Pennsylvania. But on Christmas night, 1776, the American commander recrossed the river and led a bold surprise attack on Trenton, which he easily captured from the Hessian contingent posted there. In another inspired move, Washington gained a victory at Princeton, January 3, 1776, before he withdrew to Morristown to give his dwindling army respite from the more numerous and better equipped foe. There his troops settled down for the winter, satisfied that they had given the British a taste of the fight they were prepared to make to defend their independence.

Pen-and-ink drawing of the march again Fort Washington (at today's West 184th Street, New York City). Moving south from Kings Bridge at 7 o'clock on the morning of November 16, 1776, the German mercenaries demanded and received surrender of the fort at about 3 o'clock that afternoon. More than 2,800 American soldiers were captured in this engagement.

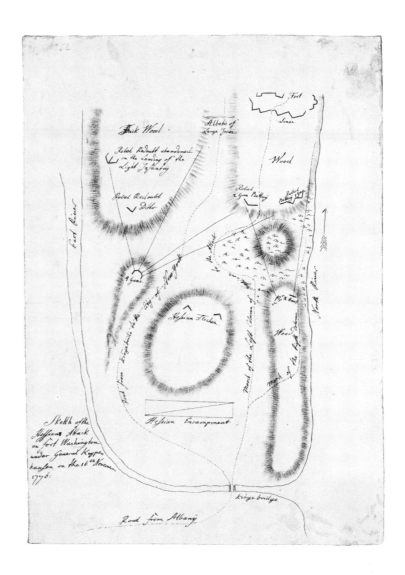

A LIST of the Killed, Wounded, and Miffing of His Majefty's Forces, under the Command of his Excellency the Honourable General HOWE, in the feveral Engagements and Skirmifhes with the PROVINCIALS, from the taking of Long-Ifland, Auguft 27th, to the Clofe of that Campaign, the 8th December, 1776.

Return of commiffioned and non-commiffioned officers, rank and file, killed, wounded, and miffing, belonging to the army under the command of his Excellency the Honourable General Howe in feveral actions, &c. with the Provincials, from the 17th of September to the 16th of November, 1776, inclufive, fpecifying the different periods, and the corps the cafualties have happened in. Head Quarters, New-York, 1ft December, 1776.

In the action at Pelham Manor, on the 18th of October, and in previous fkirmifhes, from the 17th of September inclufive.

BRITISH.

17th Regiment of Light Dragoons. 1 Drummer miffing.
1ft Battalion of Light Infantry. 1 ferjeant, 2 rank and file, killed; 1 field officer, 1 captain, 1 fubaltern, 3 ferjeants, 1 drummer or trumpeter, 23 rank and file, wounded; 2 rank and file miffing.
2d ditto, 1 rank and file, killed; 3 rank and file, wounded.
2d ditto grenadiers. 2 rank and file wounded.
4th regiment. 1 rank and file, miffing.
27th ditto. 1 rank and file, wounded.
28th ditto. 1 rank and file, wounded.
38th ditto. 1 rank and file, wounded.
55th ditto. 1 rank and file, wounded.
57th ditto. 1 rank and file, wounded.
71ft ditto. 5 rank and file, killed; 7 rank and file, wounded.
Royal Artillery. 1 ferjeant, 3 rank and file, killed.
Total. 2 ferjeants, 11 rank and file, killed. 1 field officer, 1 captain, 1 fubaltern, 3 ferjeants, 1 drummer or trumpeter, 40 rank and file, wounded. 1 drummer, 3 rank and file, miffing.

Names of the Officers killed and wounded, &c.

1ft Battalion of light infantry, captain Evelyn, of the 4th reg. killed; lieutenant colonel Mufgrave, of the 40th regiment, wounded; —— regiment, wounded.
N. B. The ferjeants and 3 rank and file of the royal artillery, returned killed, were drowned in the Eaft River by the overfetting a boat the 12th of October.

In the action the 28th of October, in paffing the Bronks River, and in previous fkirmifhes, from the 19th of October inclufive.

BRITISH.

16th regiment of light dragoons. 1 ferjeant 1 rank and file, 1 horfe, wounded. 1 rank and file, miffing.
17th ditto. 1 rank and file, 5 horfes killed. 1 fubaltern, 4 rank and file, 3 horfes wounded.
Brigade of guards. 1 rank and file killed. 2 rank and file miffing.
3d battalion of light infantry. 1 rank and file, killed. 1 fubaltern, 3 rank and file, wounded.
5th regiment. 1 rank and file killed. 1 field officer, 1 rank and file, wounded.
10th ditto. 1 rank and file, killed. 1 rank and file wounded.
28th ditto. 1 captain, 8 rank and file, killed. 1 fubaltern, 4 ferjeants, 53 rank and file, wounded.
35th ditto. 1 field officer, 1 fubaltern. 15 rank and file, killed. 2 captains, 1 fubaltern 6 ferjeants, 31 rank and file wounded. 2 rank and file, miffing.
37th ditto. 3 rank and file, killed. 2 rank and file, wounded.
45th ditto. 1 drummer, 1 rank and file, miffing.
49th ditto. 1 rank and file, 1 fubaltern, 1 ferjeant, 5 rank and file, killed; 1 fubaltern, 2 ferjeants, 17 rank and file, wounded.
71ft ditto. 2 rank and file, miffing.
New-York company. 1 rank and file, wounded.
Queen's Rangers; 20 rank and file, killed; 2 fubalterns, 8 rank and file, wounded; 28 rank and file, miffing.
Royal Artillery. 1 rank file, killed; 1 ferjeant, 1 rank and file, wounded.

Total; 1 field officer, 2 captains, 2 fubalterns, 1 ferjeant, 57 rank and file, 5 horfes, killed; 1 field officer, 2 captains, 6 fubalterns, 14 ferjeants, 123 rank and file, 4 horfes, wounded; 1 drummer, 36 rank and file, miffing.

Names of officers killed and wounded.

17th regiment of light dragoons; lieutenant Loftus, wounded.
5th regiment; lieutenant-colonel Walcot, killed.
28th ditto; captain Deering, killed; lieutenant Taylor, wounded.
35th ditto; lieutenant-colonel Carr, enfign Eagle, killed; captain Fitzgerald, capt. lieutenant Maffey, lieutenant Banks, wounded.
49th ditto; captain-lieutenant Gore, lieutenant Jocelyn, killed; lieutenant Roberts, wounded.
3d battalion of light infantry; lieutenant Swaine, of the 46th regiment, wounded.

HESSIAN CORPS, &c.

Chaffeurs; 4 rank and file, killed; 1 fubaltern, 9 rank and file, wounded; 2 rank and file, miffing.
Grenadier battalion of Linfing; 1 captain, 2 rank and file, wounded.
Grenadier battalion of Block; 1 rank and file, wounded.
Hereditary Prince's; 2 rank and file, wounded.
Lofbergh's; 6 rank and file, killed; 1 ferjeants, 39 rank and file, wounded.
Kniphaufen; 2 rank and file, wounded.
Rall's; 2 rank and file, 1 horfe, killed; 1 fubaltern, 3 rank and file, wounded.
Trumback's; 8 rank and file, miffing.
Artillery; 1 rank and file, wounded.
3d regiment of Waldeck; 13 rank and file, miffing.
Total; 12 rank and file, 1 horfe, killed; 1 captain, 4 fubalterns, 1 ferjeant, 59 rank and file, wounded; 23 rank and file, miffing.

Names of officers killed and wounded, &c.

Chaffeurs; lieutenant de Rau, wounded.
Grenadier battalion of Linfing; captain de Wefferhagen, wounded.
—— ditto of Rall; —— captain de Bull, wounded.
N. B. The 8 rank and file of the Heffian regiment of Trumback, returned miffing, were taken prifoners in Staten Ifland, the 15th of October.

In the attack of the 16th of November, when the Rebel lines and redoubts near Fort Waffington were ftormed, and that Fort furrendered, &c. with other cafualties fince the 29th of October, and preceding the 16th of November.

BRITISH.

17th regiment of dragoons; 1 rank and file, wounded.
2d battalion of light infantry; 1 ferjeant, 3 rank and file, killed; 2 ferjeants, 1 drummer, 7 rank and file, miffing.
4th regiment; 1 rank and file, wounded.
10th ditto; 1 captain, 3 rank and file, killed; 1 rank and file, wounded.
15th ditto; 1 rank and file killed; 1 rank and file, wounded.
23d ditto; 1 ferjeant, wounded.
27th ditto; 3 rank and file, miffing.
28th ditto; 1 rank and file, wounded.
38th ditto; 6 rank and file, wounded.
42d ditto; 1 ferjeant, 8 rank and file, killed; 3 fubalterns, 4 ferjeants, 66 rank and file, wounded.
52d ditto; 1 rank and file, miffing; 1 fubaltern, 1 ferjeant, wounded.
71ft ditto; 1 rank and file, wounded; 1 ferjeant, miffing.
New-York company; 1 rank and file, miffing.
Royal Artillery; 1 rank and file, killed; 1 rank and file, wounded.
Total; 1 captain, 2 ferjeants, 17 rank and file, killed; 4 fubalterns, 8 ferjeants, 2 drummer, 89 rank and file, wounded; 1 ferjeant, 5 rank and file, miffing.

Names of officers killed and wounded.

10th regiment; captain M'Intofh, killed.
42d ditto; lieutenant Alexander Grant, lieutenant Patrick Graham, lieutenant Norman M'Leod, wounded.
52d ditto; lieutenant Collier, wounded.

HESSIAN CORPS. &c.

Chaffeurs; 5 rank and file, killed; 1 fubaltern, 5 rank and file, wounded.
Grenadier battalion of Kohler; 6 rank and file, killed; 1 captain, 1 ferjeant, 33 rank and file, wounded.
Regiment de Corps; 2 rank and file, killed; 1 rank and file, wounded.
Hereditary Prince's; 2 rank and file, wounded.
Wuttginaw; 1 captain, 1 fubaltern, 1 ferjeant, 13 rank and file, killed; 2 fubalterns, 3 ferjeants, 59 rank and file, wounded.
Ditforth; 2 rank and file, wounded.
Donop; 1 rank and file, wounded.
Lofberg; 5 rank and file, killed; 1 fubaltern, 17 rank and file, wounded.
Kniphaufen; 1 captain, 6 rank and file, killed; 1 field officers, 1 fubaltern, 5 ferjeants, 58 rank and file, wounded.
Stein; 1 fubaltern, 1 rank and file, killed; 1 rank and file, wounded.
Rall; 1 drummer, 2 rank and file, killed; 1 fubaltern, 2 rank and file, wounded.
Weffembach; 4 rank and file, wounded.
Huyn; 1 fubaltern, 2 rank and file, killed; 1 fubaltern, 4 ferjeants, 21 rank and file, wounded.
Bunon; 2 rank and file, killed; 3 ferjeants, 23 rank and file, wounded.
3d regiment of Waldeck; 6 rank and file, killed; 16 rank and file, wounded.
Total; 2 captains, 3 fubalterns, 1 ferjeant, 1 drummer, 51 rank and file, killed; 1 field-officers, 1 captain, 6 fubalterns, 17 ferjeants, 246 rank and file, wounded.

Names of officers killed and wounded.

Grenadier battalion of Kouler; captain Heffe Muller, wounded.
Wittginaw's regiment; captain Modern, lieutenant Lowenfhield, killed; lieutenant de Lendaw, enfign de Ende, wounded.
Lofbergh's regiment; lieutenant de Wurmb, wounded.
Kniphaufen's ditto; captain Barkhaufen, killed; lieutenant colonel de Borcke, major de Dichow, lieutenant Brude, wounded.
Stein's ditto; lieutenant Schwein, killed; regiment of Rall; captain Walter, killed; lieutenant Kunen, enfign Werneck, wounded.
Huru's regiment; lieutenant Jufty, killed; enfign Wend, wounded.

Return of prifoners taken during the campaign, 1776.

Auguft 27. Long-Ifland.
Commiffioned officers; 3 generals, 3 colonels, 4 lieutenant colonels, 3 majors, 18 captains, 43 lieutenants, 11 enfigns.
Staff; 1 adjutant, 3 furgeons, 2 volunteers.
Privates 1006;—including 9 wounded officers, and 56 wounded privates.
September 15, 16. Ifland of New-York.
Commiffion officers; 1 colonel, 2 lieutenant colonels, 3 majors, 4 captains, 7 lieutenants.
Privates, 354.
October 12. White-Plains.
Commiffioned officers; 1 captain, 2 lieutenants.
Staff; 1 quarter-mafter.
Privates, 35.
November 16, Fort-Waffington.
Commiffioned officers, 4 colonels, 4 lieutenant-colonels, 5 majors, 46 captains, 107 lieutenants, 31 enfigns.
Staff; 1 chaplain, 2 adjutants, 2 quartermafters, 5 furgeons, 2 commiffaries, 1 engineer, 1 waggon-mafter.
Privates, 2607.
November 20. Fort-Lee.
Commiffioned officers; 1 lieutenant, 1 enfign.
Staff; 1 quarter-mafter, 3 furgeons.
Privates, 99.

TOTAL.
Commiffioned officers; 3 generals, 8 colonels, 10 lieutenant-colonels, 11 majors, 69 captains, 160 lieutenants, 43 enfigns.
Staff; 1 chaplain, 3 adjutants, 4 quartermafters, 11 furgeons, 2 commiffaries, 1 engineer, 1 waggon-mafter, 2 volunteers.
Privates, 4101.

Officers	—— ——	304
Staff	—— ——	25
Privates	—— ——	4101
(Signed) J. Lewis. } Co. of prifoners } Total.		4430

From p. 191,—p. 199.

40

Washington, together with some 2,400 troops, crossed the Delaware River about nine miles north (to the left) of Trenton on Christmas night, 1776. The legend on this pen-and-ink and water-color map pinpoints the disposition of both the American and the German troops and the surrender of the latter, garrisoned at Trenton, on the morning of December 26. From the Rochambeau Collection.

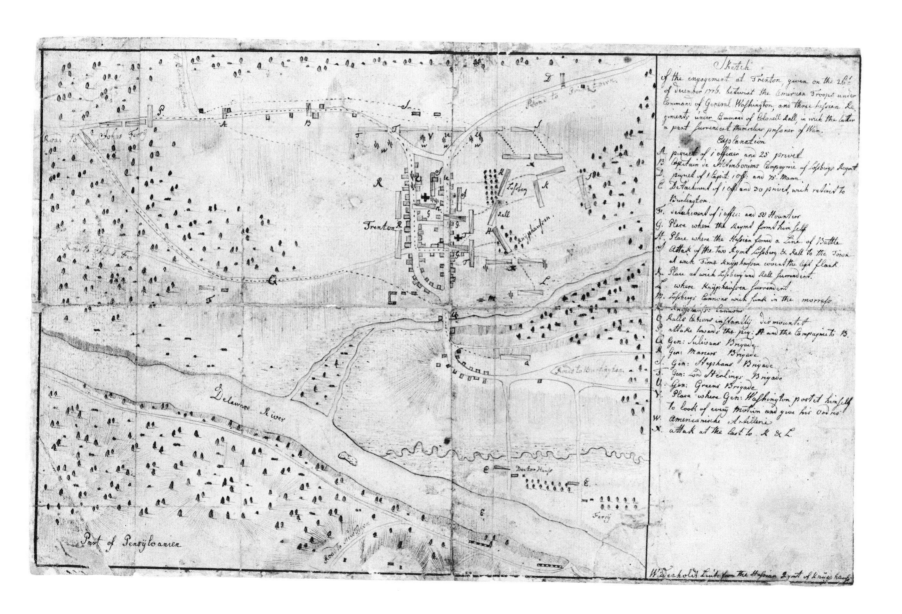

A broadside exhortation following Washington's narrow escape across the Raritan River from the pursuing British forces under the command of General Cornwallis.

On the night of September 20–21, 1777, the British mounted a surprise bayonet attack against Gen. Anthony Wayne's troops, bivouacked about two miles southwest of Paoli, Pa. The encounter, which is shown on this manuscript map, was characterized "the Paoli Massacre," after the town located at the center of the map along the Lancaster-Philadelphia road.

To the north, at the top of the map, Valley Creek is the stream that led to Valley Forge, the site of George Washington's winter encampment later that same year. From the Faden Collection.

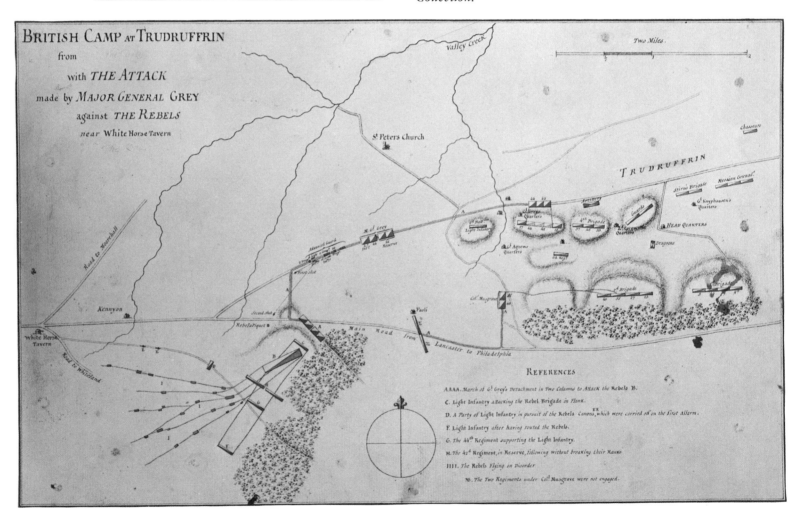

42

Gen. Anthony Wayne, a soldier with a reputation for boldness and impetuosity, repaid the surprise attack on his troops at Paoli with an impressive victory at Stony Point, N.Y., in 1779. Engraving by John Norman, in An Impartial History of the War in America (Boston, 1782). LC-USZ62-45242

This engraving in The Westminster Magazine for February 1778 is a British view of the deterioration of British power (the lion) and British commerce (the cow), due at least in part to the military laxity of the brothers Howe, who are shown across the ocean fast asleep in Philadelphia. During the spring and summer of 1778 the British ministry accepted the resignations of Adm. Richard Howe, commander of British naval forces in America, and Gen. William Howe, commander of the British army in America. LC-USZ62-39591

Gen. John Burgoyne, commander of the British forces defeated at Saratoga. Because of his civility toward his troops, Burgoyne's soldiers nicknamed him "Gentleman Johnny." Engraving by [Robert?] Pollard, in James Murray, An Impartial History of the Present War in America (London, 1780). LC-USZ62-45354

The British encampment at Saratoga, after the Battle at Bemis Heights on October 7, 1777. Simon Frazer's death in this battle has been attributed to the lengendary Continental rifleman, Timothy Murphy. To the left can be seen the boat bridge across which the British troops coming down from Canada crossed the Hudson (but which in fact had been dismantled on September 15, two days after the crossing). Etching in Thomas Anburey's Travels Through the Interior Parts of America (London, 1789). LC-USZ62-31881

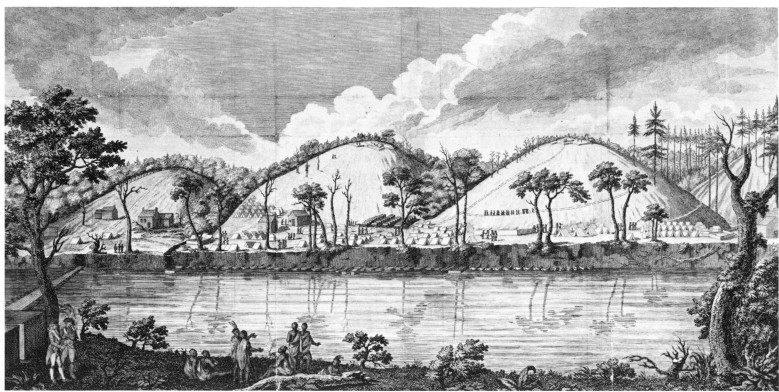

The campaign of 1777 saw two major actions—both significant, but not equally so. The lesser of the two, the British capture of Philadelphia on September 26, forced the Continental Congress to withdraw to York, Pa., but control of Philadelphia was no more decisive than the earlier occupation of Boston had been. Of greater consequence, considered by some the most important single event of the war, was the battle at Saratoga, N.Y., in October. There, on the 17th a British-Hessian force of more than 5,000 troops laid down its weapons and surrendered. The victory at Saratoga was a great boost to American morale, but it was of even greater interest in France, where it was interpreted as proof of the viability and durability of the American cause. Consequently, on February 6, 1778, the government of Louis XVI recognized American independence and signed a treaty of alliance with the American commissioners.

During the following two years there were few decisive military operations. In December 1777 Washington quartered his army for the winter at Valley Forge, Pa., where despite physical hardship the American soldiers were shaped into a disciplined force. Subsequently, the troops who experienced Valley Forge formed the core of a veteran army which rose to the occasion in 1781 to capture an army of British invaders in Virginia.

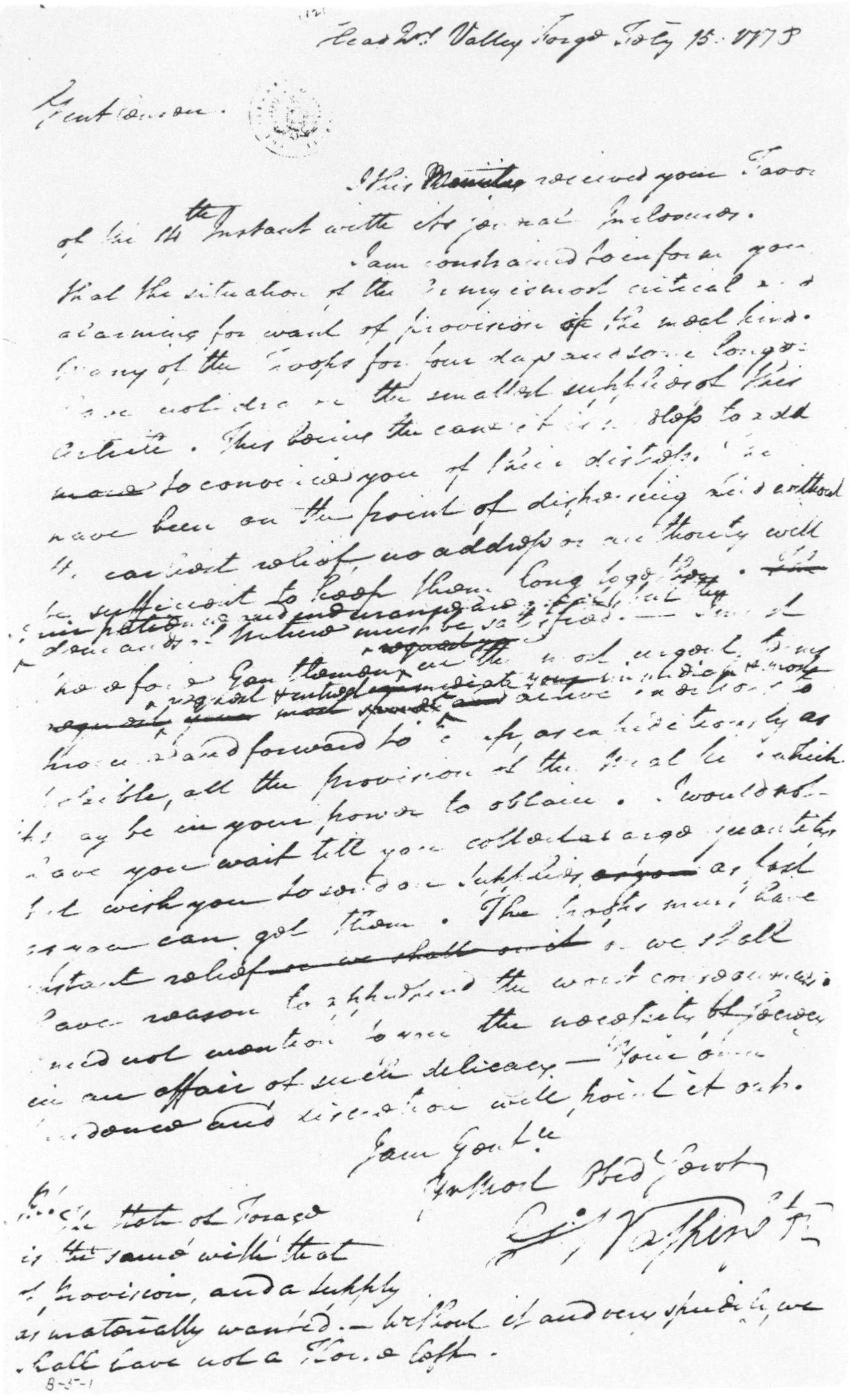
Head Qrs Valley Forge Feby 15. 1778

Gentlemen.

This Minute received your Favor of the 14th Instant with its journal Inclosures.

I am constrained to inform you that the situation of the Army is most critical and alarming for want of provision of the meat kind. Many of the Troops for four days and some longer have not drawn the smallest supplies of that Article. This being the case ... more to convince you of their distress. They have been on the point of dispersing and without the earliest relief no address or authority will be sufficient to keep them long together. ...

Shown is a draft letter addressed to Robert L. Hooper, deputy quartermaster general, and two of his aides, in which the American commander in chief describes the "situation of the Army" at Valley Forge as "most critical and alarming for want of provision of the meat kind." Washington warned that his troops "have been on the point of dispersing and without the earliest relief, no address or authority will be sufficient to keep them long together." From the Washington papers.

Friedrich Wilhelm von Steuben, formerly a Prussian army officer, developed a program to train and discipline the Continental troops at Valley Forge. In 1778 he was appointed inspector general of the American army. Engraving, after a life drawing by Pierre Eugene DuSimitière, in Portraits of the Generals, Ministers, Magistrates, Members of Congress and Others, Who Have Rendered Themselves Illustrious in the Revolution of the United States of North America *(London, 1783). LC-USZ62-45483*

Gen. John Glover. Engraving by H. B. Hall, after a 1790 pencil sketch from life by John Trumbull. LC-USZ62-3590

Marquis de Lafayette, a French nobleman who at the age of 19 joined Washington's command soon after arriving in America in the summer of 1777. In 1781 he and General Cornwallis maneuvered in Virginia, leading ultimately to Cornwallis' fortifications at Yorktown and Gloucester Point. Engraving by Noel le Mire after a painting by Jean Le Paon. LC-USZ62-934

Following an unsuccessful attempt in August 1778 to land French forces at Newport in a combined effort with Gen. John Sullivan's Continental troops to expel the British from Rhode Island, the French fleet put out to sea. This wash drawing shows Admiral D'Estaing's flagship, demasted in a violent storm, under attack by a British man o' war. From the Ozanne Collection. LC-USZ62-902

Le Vaisseau le Languedoc dematé par le coup de vent dans la nuit du 12. attaqué par un Vaisseau de Guerre Anglois l'après midy du 13 Aout 1778

Le Languedoc dematé de tous mats, son Gouvernail en rompu, il a appareillé deux petites voiles de sa chaloupe pour tacher de diminuer les roulis; mais il ne peut ni arrier ni gouverner, il fait feu de ses cinq Canons et retraite un canoy de 36. a été demonté des la premiere volée de l'ennemi dont les boulets l'enfilent de long en long en perçant le tableau de l'arriere partie la moins forte du Vaisseau vont jusqua la Gatte.

Le Renown de cinquante Canons Capitaine Dawson enfilant le Languedoc en le battant de vingt cinq pieces de Canon.

Nta. 1 Le Lord Howe pendant la chasse avoit quitté son vaisseau pour la frégate l'Apollon; elle fut aussi dematé pendant le coup de vent.

2 Le Renown cessa de lui même le combat contre le Languedoc, rien ne l'empechoit de le continuer; la soirée fut longue et la nuit très belle.

During this two-year interval the Americans had difficulty with enlistments and military supplies, and the British were compelled to divert some of their resources to meet France's entry into the war. In the summer of 1778 French reinforcements commanded by Comte d'Estaing arrived off the American coast. Just three weeks before their arrival, the British evacuated Philadelphia, and the Americans, under Washington and Charles Lee, engaged the retiring enemy on June 28 at Monmouth Court House, N.J. The confused fight that followed, which has been described as a draw, was the last important military encounter in the North.

A kaleidoscopic view of the war in America during the next year and a half would show, among other events, an American naval fiasco on Maine's Penobscot River balanced by the triumph of John Paul Jones' *Bonhomme Richard* over the *Serapis* in British waters; the British capture of Savannah and Charleston in the South as against George Rogers Clark's conquest of the Illinois country; and the treasonable attempt by Benedict Arnold to surrender West Point to the British juxtaposed with the victory of southern militiamen over Carolina loyalists at Kings Mountain, S.C.

49

Gen. Charles Lee, appointed second in command to Washington. His hesitancy in executing orders to attack during the battle of Monmouth Court House led to his court-martial. Mezzotint engraving published by C. Shepherd, London, 1775. LC-USZ62-3617

Pinpointed on this pen-and-ink and watercolor map is the spot where Washington encountered the retreating Charles Lee, reportedly condemned him for his conduct, and relieved him of his command.

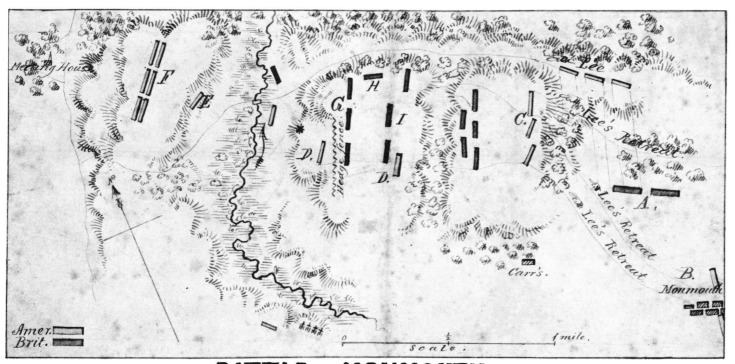

BATTLE of MONMOUTH. *June 28. 1778.*

A. Left wing of the British the night before.
B. American troops near Court house.
C. First posit.ⁿ taken by Genl. Lee in his retreat.
D. Later positions of Genl. Lee

E. Last position of Genl. Lee.
F. Disposition of the Army by Washington after he met Lee.
* The spot where they met.
G. Principal Battle.

H & I. British pos.ⁿˢ after the action.

At one point in the battle between John Paul Jones' Bonhomme Richard *and* Richard Pearson's Serapis, *the two ships came so close to one another that Jones was able to lash them together. While they were struggling in this position the* Alliance, *a warship attached to Jones' squadron and commanded by a French antagonist of his, shelled the* Richard, *apparently intentionally, killing several of her crew.*

This etching by B. F. Leizalt (probably copied from an engraving published in 1781), after a drawing by Richard Paton, incorrectly dates the action one day earlier than its actual occurrence. LC-USZ62-112

John Paul Jones, captain in the Continental navy. Contemporary engraving by Carl Guttenberg after a drawing by C. J. Notté. LC-USZ62-45184

A page from a letter written by John Paul Jones to Robert Morris, dated at Amsterdam, October 13, 1779, describing the encounter between the Bonhomme Richard *and the* Serapis. *From the Morris papers.*

between the Bon Homme Richard and the Serapis was dreadfull: an hour from the Commencement I found that I had to deal with a far Superior force and the Serapis being a much more manageable Ship than the Bon Homme Richard I was under the necessity of closing with her. — I found means to get the Enemies Bowsprit over the Bon Homme Richards Quarter, and immediately made him fast to the Mizen mast — the Ships then swang along side of one another, the Enemies Stern being Opposite to our Bow and the yard being locked. In that Situation the Action Continued two hours and a half both Ships being on fire for the greatest part of the time and the Bon Homme Richard making as much water as all the Pumps could discharge — at last the Alliance appeared but not to our Assistance; for instead of laying the Enemy along side or of assisting us with fresh Men, he sailed round and fired into the Bon Homme Richard, even after every tongue had exclaimed that he fired into the wrong Ship and I had hoisted a signal which could not be mistaken, he killed a number of our Men and Mortally wounded a good Officer. — at last the Enemy Struck the English Flagg — but the Victory

was

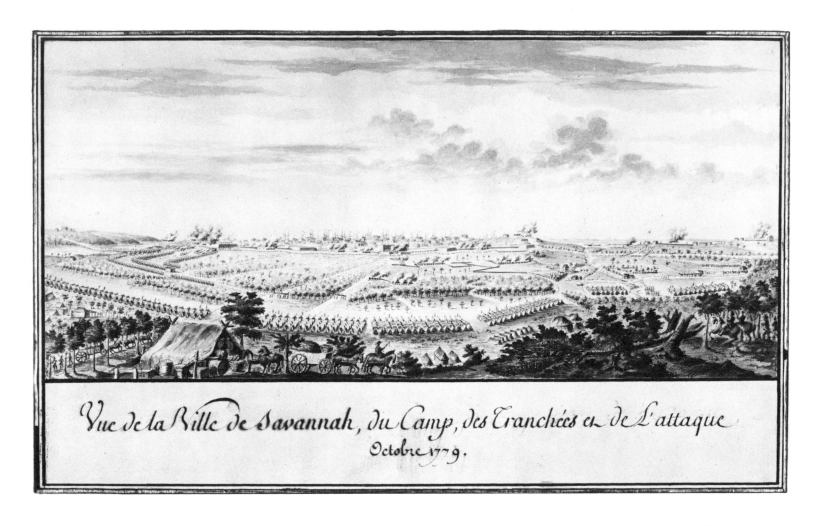

Vue de la Ville de Savannah, du Camp, des Tranchées et de L'attaque Octobre 1779.

Shown in the foreground of this wash drawing are the American and French camps behind their zigzag siege trenches, looking toward the British fortifications, the town of Savannah, and the Savannah River. On October 8, 1779, after having besieged Savannah for about two weeks, Admiral d'Estaing, commander of the French forces, changed tactics and ordered an attack against the British-held city. The attack failed badly, with perhaps 1,100 French and American troops killed or wounded, while British casualties may not have exceeded 100. Among those killed was Casimir Pulaski, a Polish nobleman who had joined the American cause in the summer of 1777. From the Ozanne Collection. LC-USZ62-11898

Tappaan the 1st October. 1780

Sir

Buoyd above the Terror of Death by the Consciousness of a Life devoted to honorable pursuits and Stained with no Action that can give me Remorse, I trust the request I make to your Excellency at this serious period and which is to Soften my last moments will not be rejected.

Sympathy towards a Soldier will surely induce Your Excellency and

and a military Tribunal to adopt the Mode of my death to the feelings of a Man of honour.

Let me hope Sir, that if aught in my Character impresses you with Esteem towards me, if aught in my Misfortunes marks me as the Victim of Policy and not of Resentment I shall experience the Operation of these feelings in your Breast by being informed that I am not to die on a Gibbet

I have the honour to be

Your Excellency's
Most obedient and
most humble Servant
John André Adj.
to the British Army

Major André, aide-de-camp to Gen. Henry Clinton, was captured on September 23, 1780, while trying to return to the British lines with the information about West Point that Benedict Arnold had given to him. Washington did not reply to André's note, written on the day before he was hanged. From the Washington papers.

BY
Brigadier-General ARNOLD,
A PROCLAMATION.

To the Officers and Soldiers of the Continental Army who have the real Interest of their Country at Heart, and who are determined to be no longer the Tools and Dupes of Congress, or of France.

HAVING reason to believe that the principles I have avowed, in my address to the public of the 7th instant, animated the greatest part of this continent, I rejoice in the opportunity I have of inviting you to join His Majesty's Arms.

His Excellency Sir *Henry Clinton* has authorized me to raise a corps of cavalry and infantry, who are to be clothed, subsisted, and paid as the other troops are in the British service, and those who bring in horses, arms, or accoutrements, are to be paid their value, or have liberty to sell them: To every non-commissioned officer and private a bounty of THREE GUINEAS will be given, and as the Commander in Chief is pleased to allow me to nominate the officers, I shall with infinite satisfaction embrace this opportunity of advancing men whose valour I have witnessed, and whose principles are favourable to an union with *Britain*, and TRUE AMERICAN LIBERTY.

The rank they obtain in the King's service will bear a proportion to their former rank, and the number of men they bring with them.

It is expected that a Lieutenant-Colonel of cavalry will bring with him, or recruit in a reasonable time, 75 men,

Major of *HORSE* - 50 men.		Lieut. Col. of *INFANTRY* - 75 men.
Captain of ditto - - - 30		Major of ditto - - - - - - - - - - 50
Lieutenant of ditto - 15		Captain of ditto - - - - - - - - - 30
Cornet of ditto - - - 12		Lieutenant of ditto - - - - - - - 15
Serjeant of ditto - - - 6		Ensign of ditto - - - - - - - - - 12
		Serjeant of ditto - - - - - - - - - 6

N. B. Each Field Officer will have a Company.

Great as this encouragement must appear to such as have suffered every distress of want of pay, hunger and nakedness, from the neglect, contempt, and corruption of Congress, they are nothing to the motives which I expect will influence the brave and generous minds I hope to have the honour to command.

I wish to lead a chosen band of Americans to the attainment of peace, liberty, and safety (that first object in taking the field) and with them to share in the glory of rescuing our native country from the grasping hand of *France*, as well as from the ambitious and interested views of a desperate party among ourselves, who, in listening to *French* overtures, and rejecting those from *Great-Britain*, have brought the colonies to the very brink of destruction.

Friends, fellow soldiers, and citizens, arouse, and judge for yourselves,—reflect on what you have lost,—consider to what you are reduced, and by your courage repel the ruin that still threatens you.

Your country once was happy, and had the proffered peace been embraced, your last two years of misery had been spent in peace and plenty, and repairing the desolations of a quarrel that would have set the interest of *Great-Britain* and *America* in its true light, and cemented their friendship; whereas, you are now the prey of avarice, the scorn of your enemies, and the pity of your friends.

You were promised LIBERTY by the leaders of your affairs; but is there an individual in the enjoyment of it, saving your oppressors? Who among you dare speak, or write what he thinks, against the tyranny which has robbed you of your property, imprisons your persons, drags you to the field of battle, and is daily deluging your country with your blood?

You are flattered with independency as preferable to a redress of grievances, and for that shadow, instead of real felicity, are sunk into all the wretchedness of poverty by the rapacity of your own rulers. Already are you disqualified to support the pride of character they taught you to aim at, and must inevitably shortly belong to one or other of the great powers their folly and wickedness have drawn into conflict. Happy for you that you may still become the fellow-subjects of *Great-Britain*, if you nobly disdain to be the vassals of *France*.

What is *America* now but a land of widows, orphans, and beggars?—and should the parent nation cease her exertions to deliver you, what security remains to you even for the enjoyment of the consolations of that religion for which your fathers braved the ocean, the heathen, and the wilderness? Do you know that the eye which guides this pen lately saw your mean and profligate Congress at mass for the soul of a Roman Catholic in Purgatory, and participating in the rites of a Church, against whose antichristian corruptions your pious ancestors would have witnessed with their blood.

As to you who have been soldiers in the continental army, can you at this day want evidence that the funds of your country are exhausted, or that the managers have applied them to their own private uses? In either case you surely can no longer continue in their service with honour or advantage; yet you have hitherto been their supporters of that cruelty, which, with an equal indifference to your, as well as to the labour and blood of others, is devouring a country, which, from the moment you quit their colours, will be redeemed from their tyranny.

But what need of arguments to such as feel infinitely more misery than tongue can express. I therefore only add my promise of the most affectionate welcome and attention to all who are disposed to join me in the measures necessary to close the scene of our afflictions, which, intolerable as they are, must continue to increase until we have the wisdom (shewn of late by *Ireland*) in being contented with the liberality of the Parent Country, who still offers her protection, with the immediate restoration of our ancient privileges, civil ... ption from all taxes, but such as we shall think fit to impose on ourselves.

B. ARNOLD.

Throughout the period the frontiers were ravaged by small-scale engagements in which the American Indians participated, predominantly as allies of the British. Some of the tribes managed to defy pressure from both sides and remain neutral. The principal American campaign against hostile Indians was launched from Pennsylvania against the Iroquois of western New York by Gen. John Sullivan in 1779. Although little fighting occurred, Sullivan destroyed the Indians' villages and crops and rendered them ineffective for the remainder of the war.

Although Benedict Arnold's plan to deliver West Point to the British had gone awry, his effort was rewarded in part with a commission as Brigadier General of the British army. This broadside, dated October 20, 1780, had only a limited effect in enticing Continential soldiers to the side of Great Britain.

John Sullivan, Continental commander of the ill-fated Franco-American attack at Newport, R.I., in August 1778, led an attack in 1779 against the Iroquois supporters of the British army, destroying their villages and crops in the Mohawk Valley. Mezzotint engraving published by Thomas Hart, London, 1776. LC-USZ62-39567

Tayadaneega (otherwise known as Joseph Brant), a Mohawk chief educated at the Indian School (later Dartmouth College) in New Hampshire, held a British commission as Colonel of Indians. In the late 1770's and early 1780's he led the Iroquois on a series of devastating raids against colonial towns on the New York frontier. Engraving by John R. Smith, 1779, after a portrait by George Romney painted in 1775 while Tayadaneega was visiting England. LC-USZ62-20488

The first full-scale effort to end the war by talking rather than by fighting was a conference on Staten Island in September 1776 between Lord Howe and a committee of the Continental Congress. Thereafter, the British made desultory overtures to the Americans, none of which elicited serious consideration. In 1778 a new British peace commission, headed by the Earl of Carlisle, was appointed to thwart American ratification of the Franco-American treaty, but even before the commissioners arrived in America, Congress denounced any effort to come to terms with them.

British efforts to negotiate an end to the American rebellion were paralleled by the secret activities of France, before her entry in the war, to supply the Americans and to deal her ancient foe a blow by aiding the rebels. The most significant of these activities was the establishment of an ostensibly private commercial house, Hortalez & Cie., through which the French government channeled to the Americans great quantities of muskets, gunpowder, blankets, and other desperately needed and thankfully received war material. Although such aid was appreciated, Congress in September 1776 appointed three representatives, Benjamin Franklin, Arthur Lee, and Silas Deane, to enlist France's public rather than secret assistance. As a result of the victory at Saratoga, they succeeded in February 1778 in signing treaties of alliance and of amity and commerce with the government of Louis XVI.

First page of the printed text of one of the two treaties negotiated by France and the United States following news of the American victory at Saratoga. This one was published in Paris, chez P. G. Simon, Imprimeur du Parlement. The other treaty, that of a "conditional and defensive alliance," was to become operative only if England and France went to war.

THE COMMISSIONERS

Comte de Vergennes, foreign minister of France, with whom Benjamin Franklin negotiated the treaty of alliance. Engraving by Vincenzio Vangelisti after a painting by Antoine Callet. LC-USZ62-45183

Benjamin Franklin at 56. Mezzotint engraving by Edward Fisher after a painting in 1762 by Mason Chamberlin. LC-USZ62-1434

Subsequently, John Adams was appointed minister to the Netherlands, where he secured Dutch recognition of American independence and arranged for vitally needed loans. John Jay was sent to Madrid in an unsuccessful effort to secure additional financial aid and a recognition of independence from the Spanish monarchy. At other times during the war, missions were dispatched to Russia, Prussia, Austria, and Tuscany, but none had any significant impact.

The American success at Saratoga was matched by Benjamin Franklin's conquest of the salons of Paris. The venerable American ambassador, by shrewdly playing on the emotions of the French, became a national celebrity whose pictures and proverbs adorned the humblest cottages. The Franklin fad, in fact, became so excessive that Louis XVI satirized it by presenting ladies of the court with chamber pots with the doctor's face painted on the bottom. Franklin capitalized on his popularity by obtaining a series of large loans and shipments of supplies from the French ministry, without which the victory of the colonists might not have been possible.

The Home Fronts

The Revolutionary War did not dominate the consciousness of Britons to the extent that it did that of Americans. The British intelligentsia pondered two seminal works which appeared in 1776: Adam Smith's *Wealth of Nations* and Edward Gibbon's *Decline and Fall of the Roman Empire*. The populace diverted itself with Goldsmith, Garrick, and Sheridan; the scientific community speculated about James Cook's explorations, which Benjamin Franklin assisted in 1779 by supplying the captain with a certificate of safe passage to prevent his capture by American warships.

But the war, if not a central issue, was an important one, and in England, as in America, opinion was divided over the policies of the ministers of George III. Before warfare broke out, men like William Pitt and Edmund Burke espoused the colonial cause, and after the fighting started they persisted in their opposition to administration policies. Some English dissidents, notably John Wilkes and Isaac Barré, became folk heroes to the colonists. But if there were those who favored the American cause before 1775, clearly they were in a minority, and after 1778, when France allied herself with the United States, Englishmen closed ranks behind the war effort.

The American Revolution was fought on American soil, and in a very significant sense it touched the lives of most colonists. There must have been very few indeed who did not know someone, or the family of someone, who had been wounded or killed in battle. Throughout the war foraging parties of both American and British armies appropriated the products of American farms, and thousands experienced the indiscriminate pillaging of marauding

Edmund Burke, Member of Parliament from 1766 to 1794. His speeches supporting the American position on taxation and opposing the "Intolerable Acts" of 1774 were warmly received in the colonies. Mezzotint engraving, 1770, by James Watson after a painting by Joshua Reynolds. LC-USZ62-48733

William Pitt, Earl of Chatham, eloquent opponent of Great Britain's coercive policy toward the colonies. Mezzotint engraving, 1766, by Richard Houston after a painting by William Hoare. LC-USZ62-28073

A British comment on the economic effects of long-continuing warfare. In the middle ground George III goes hunting, while across the sea in the background flames engulf Norfolk (burned January 1, 1776) and Esopus (now Kingston), N.Y. (burned in October 1777). The "To Let" signs reflect the dismal fact that in 1779 there were more than 1,000 empty houses in London. LC-USZ62-1520

the Delegates to be upon Honor to meet punctually at 10 OClo. A Report respecting Canada was produced — Dr. Franklin shewed me to day a Pattern Paper containing 6 or 8 Sorts of Cloths lately manufactured at one or both of the Company Manufactories of Philada — Cols. Heard & Waterbury are to disarm the Tories of Queens County on Oath that they have deli:vered up all their Arms & ammunit. and to imprison all that refuse the Oath, these Tories are not to quit their Country without a Pass certifying that they are welldisposed to the Ame:rican Cause — all to be considered as Tories who voted agt. sending Dele:gates to the present N York Convention no Lawyer may bring an Action for

them, Quære Whether People are not forbid to trade with these Tories. the Cols. are also to seize certain Persons named in a List & confine them till further Order of Congress — 500 Dolls and 200 lb. of Powder allowed for the Expedition (which was afterwards well executed by the Jersey Militia only those of Connect. being countermanded)

Monday 8 January — Votes of Sa:turday read as were Letters from Gen. Schuyler and Montgomery, the latter, it seems, was before Quebec the 5th. of Dec. & expects Success in his intended Storm, he demands 10,000 Men to defend Canada, A Report consisting of several Articles about that Country, was agreed to, then it

British and Hessian troops. Inflation affected everyone, so much so that by the summer of 1781 to say that something was "not worth a continental" (i.e., paper currency issued by the Congress) was to say that it was virtually worthless.

If the patriots suffered, the loyalists suffered even more. Before the actual outbreak of fighting many experienced personal indignities; after 1775, they were harrassed, fined, imprisoned, and exiled. By the war's end, more than 60,000 loyalists had been driven from America.

John Wilkes, an English radical whose stormy political career in opposition to King George III in the 1760's and thereafter endeared him to many colonists as a champion of "liberty" and "the rights of Englishmen." Mezzotint engraving, 1764, by James Watson after a painting by Robert E. Pine. LC-USZ62-48734

This diary entry for January 6, 1776, reflects the hardening attitudes and restrictive measures applied to those Americans who remained loyal to Great Britain. The diarist, Richard Smith, represented New Jersey in the Continental Congress from September 1774 to June 1776; he recorded much information about the activities of Congress not available elsewhere. From the Personal Miscellany Collection.

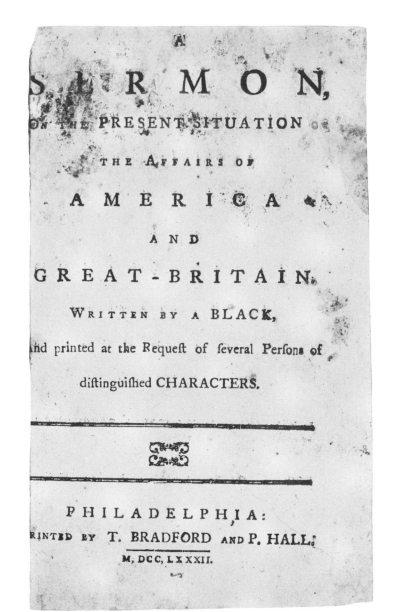

A

SERMON,

ON THE PRESENT SITUATION OF

THE AFFAIRS OF

AMERICA

AND

GREAT-BRITAIN.

WRITTEN BY A BLACK,

And printed at the Requeſt of ſeveral Perſons of

diſtinguiſhed CHARACTERS.

PHILADELPHIA:

PRINTED BY T. BRADFORD AND P. HALL.

M,DCC,LXXXII.

Charles Thomson of Philadelphia, secretary of Congress from 1774 to 1789. This engraving, after a life drawing by Pierre Eugene DuSimitière, was first published in Paris in 1781; it is taken here from Portraits of the Generals, Ministers, Magistrates, Members of Congress and Others, Who Have Rendered Themselves Illustrious in the Revolution of the United States of North America *(London, 1783). LC-USZ62-44786*

On page 9 of this 1782 pamphlet the anonymous author wrote:
"And now my virtuous fellow citizens, let me entreat you, that, after you have rid yourselves of the British yoke, that you will also emancipate those who have been all their life time subject to bondage."

An undated broadside, in which the anonymous author glories in the deeds of famed heroines of the past and observes that "if opinion and manners did not forbid us to march to glory by the same paths as the men, we should at least equal, and sometimes surpass them in our love for the public good."

The SENTIMENTS of an
AMERICAN WOMAN.

ON the commencement of actual war, the Women of America manifested a firm resolution to contribute as much as could depend on them, to the deliverance of their country. Animated by the purest patriotism, they are sensible of sorrow at this day, in not offering more than barren wishes for the success of so glorious a Revolution. They aspire to render themselves more really useful; and this sentiment is universal from the north to the south of the Thirteen United States. Our ambition is kindled by the fame of those heroines of antiquity, who have rendered their sex illustrious, and have proved to the universe, that, if the weakness of our Constitution, if opinion and manners did not forbid us to march to glory by the same paths as the Men, we should at least equal, and sometimes surpass them in our love for the public good. I glory in all that which my sex has done great and commendable. I call to mind with enthusiasm and with admiration, all those acts of courage, of constancy and patriotism, which history has transmitted to us: The people favoured by Heaven, preserved from destruction by the virtues, the zeal and the resolution of Deborah, of Judith, of Esther! The fortitude of the mother of the Macchabees, in giving up her sons to die before her eyes: Rome saved from the fury of a victorious enemy by the efforts of Volumnia; and other Roman Ladies: So many famous sieges where the Women have been seen forgetting the weakness of their sex, building new walls, digging trenches with their feeble hands; furnishing arms to their defenders, they themselves darting the missile weapons on the enemy, resigning the ornaments of their apparel, and their fortune, to fill the public treasury, and to hasten the deliverance of their country; burying themselves under its ruins; throwing themselves into the flames rather than submit to the disgrace of humiliation before a proud enemy.

Born for liberty, disdaining to bear the irons of a tyrannic Government, we associate ourselves to the grandeur of those Sovereigns, cherished and revered, who have held with so much splendour the scepter of the greatest States, The Batildas, the Elizabeths, the Maries, the Catharines, who have extended the empire of liberty, and contented to reign by sweetness and justice, have broken the chains of slavery, forged by tyrants in the times of ignorance and barbarity. The Spanish Women, do they not make, at this moment, the most patriotic sacrifices, to encrease the means of victory in the hands of their Sovereign. He is a friend to the French Nation. They are our allies. We call to mind, doubly interested, that it was a French Maid who kindled up amongst her fellow-citizens, the flame of patriotism buried under long misfortunes: It was the Maid of Orleans who drove from the kingdom of France the ancestors of those same British, whose odious yoke we have just shaken off; and whom it is necessary that we drive from this Continent.

But I must limit myself to the recollection of this small number of atchievements. Who knows if persons disposed to censure, and sometimes too severely with regard to us, may not disapprove our appearing acquainted even with the actions of which our sex boasts? We are at least certain, that he cannot be a good citizen who will not applaud our efforts for the relief of the armies which defend our lives, our possessions, our liberty? The situation of our soldiery has been represented to me; the evils inseparable from war, and the firm and generous spirit which has enabled them to support these. But it has been said, that they may apprehend, that, in the course of a long war, the view of their distresses may be lost, and their services be forgotten. Forgotten! never; I can answer in the name of all my sex. Brave Americans, your disinterestedness, your courage, and your constancy will always be dear to America, as long as she shall preserve her virtue.

We know that at a distance from the theatre of war, if we enjoy any tranquility, it is the fruit of your watchings, your labours, your dangers. If I live happy in the midst of my family; if my husband cultivates his field, and reaps his harvest in peace; if, surrounded with my children, I myself nourish the youngest, and press it to my bosom, without being affraid of seeing myself separated from it, by a ferocious enemy; if the house in which we dwell; if our barns, our orchards are safe at the present time from the hands of those incendiaries, it is to you that we owe it. And shall we hesitate to evidence to you our gratitude? Shall we hesitate to wear a cloathing more simple; hair dressed less elegant, while at the price of this small privation, we shall deserve your benedictions. Who, amongst us, will not renounce with the highest pleasure, those vain ornaments, when she shall consider that the valiant defenders of America will be able to draw some advantage from the money which she may have laid out in these; that they will be better defended from the rigours of the seasons, that after their painful toils, they will receive some extraordinary and unexpected relief; that these presents will perhaps be valued by them at a greater price, when they will have it in their power to say: *This is the offering of the Ladies.* The time is arrived to display the same sentiments which animated us at the beginning of the Revolution, when we renounced the use of teas, however agreeable to our taste, rather than receive them from our persecutors; when we made it appear to them that we placed former necessaries in the rank of superfluities, when our liberty was interested; when our republican and laborious hands spun the flax, prepared the linen intended for the use of our soldiers; when exiles and fugitives we supported with courage all the evils which are the concomitants of war. Let us not lose a moment; let us be engaged to offer the homage of our gratitude at the altar of military valour, and you, our brave deliverers, while mercenary slaves combat to cause you to share with them, the irons with which they are loaded, receive with a free hand our offering, the purest which can be presented to your virtue,

By An AMERICAN WOMAN.

The war shifted to the South with the British capture of Savannah in 1779 and Charleston in 1780. In South Carolina a British victory at Camden in the summer of 1780 was offset by American victories at Kings Mountain and Cowpens that fall and winter. After a pyrrhic victory at Guilford Courthouse, N.C., in March 1781, Lord Cornwallis, the British commander, was forced to withdraw to the coast, where he could be supplied and reinforced by the British navy. Moving to Yorktown, Va., in the summer of 1781, Cornwallis in October experienced the fate that had befallen Burgoyne four years earlier almost to the day at Saratoga. Trapped between the fleet of the French admiral Comte de Grasse and the combined Franco-American armies of Washington and Rochambeau, Cornwallis surrendered his troops on October 20, 1781.

STATE OF NEW-HAMPSHIRE.

In the HOUSE of REPRESENTATIVES,

July 3, 1781.

THE Committee to form a Table or Scale of Depreciation for this State, reported as their Opinion, That all Contracts previous to the last Day of January 1777, shall be considered as Silver and Gold ; and all Contracts for Paper Money from the last Day of January 1777, to the last day of June 1781, to be computed in the following Manner.

	Continental Paper in 1777.		Continental Paper 1778.		Continental Paper 1779.		Continental Paper 1780.		Continental Paper 1781.	
	£.	£.	£.	£.	£.	£.	£.	£.	£.	£.
January,	Equal.		325	100	742	100	2-34	100	7500	100
February,	104	100	350	Ditto	868	Ditto	3322	Ditto	7500	Ditto
March,	106	Ditto	375	Ditto	1000	Ditto	3736	Ditto	7500	Ditto
April,	110	Ditto	400	Ditto	1104	Ditto	4000	Ditto	7500	Ditto
May,	114	Ditto	400	Ditto	1215	Ditto	4800	Ditto	7500	Ditto
June,	120	Ditto	400	Ditto	1342	Ditto	5700	Ditto	12000	Ditto
July,	125	Ditto	425	Ditto	1477	Ditto	6000	Ditto		
August,	150	Ditto	450	Ditto	1630	Ditto	6300	Ditto		
September,	175	Ditto	475	Ditto	1800	Ditto	6500	Ditto		
October,	275	Ditto	500	Ditto	2030	Ditto	6700	Ditto		
November,	300	Ditto	545	Ditto	2308	Ditto	7000	Ditto		
December,	310	Ditto	634	Ditto	2393	Ditto	7300	Ditto		

Which Report being read and considered, VOTED, That it be received and accepted.

Sent up for Concurrence.

JOHN LANGDON, Speaker.

In COUNCIL, the same Day read and concurred.

E. THOMPSON, Secretary.

Copy examined by

J. PEARSON, D. Secretary.

A graphic depiction of the depreciation of Continental currency between January 1777 (when £100 silver equaled £100 Continental) and June 1781 (when the same £100 silver equaled £12,000 Continental).

In March 1778 Henry Clinton replaced William Howe as commander of the British army in America. This proclamation announcing clemency for repentant rebels appeared 20 days after his capture of Charleston, S.C., two years later. Marriot Arbuthnot was, at the time, commander of British naval forces in America.

SOUTH-CAROLINA.

By Sir HENRY CLINTON, Knight of the Bath, General of His Majesty's Forces, and MARIOT ARBUTHNOT, Esquire, Vice-Admiral of the Blue, His Majesty's Commissioners to restore Peace and good Government in the several Colonies in Rebellion in North-America.

PROCLAMATION.

HIS MAJESTY having been pleased, by His Letters Patent, under the Great Seal of Great-Britain, to appoint us to be his Commissioners, to restore the Blessings of Peace and Liberty to the several Colonies in Rebellion in America, WE do hereby make public his most gracious Intentions, and in Obedience to his Commands, DO DECLARE, to such of his deluded Subjects, as have been perverted from their Duty by the Factious Arts of self-interested and ambitious Men, That they will still be received with Mercy and Forgiveness, if they immediately return to their Allegiance, and a due Obedience to those Laws and that Government which they formerly boasted was their best Birthright and noblest Inheritance, and upon a due Experience of the Sincerity of their Professions, a full and free Pardon will be granted for the treasonable Offences which they have heretofore committed, in such Manner and Form as his Majesty's Commission doth direct.

NEVERTHELESS, it is only to those, who, convinced of their Errors, are firmly resolved to return to and Support that Government under which they were formerly so happy and free, that these gracious Offers are once more renewed, and therefore those Persons are excepted, who, notwithstanding their present hopeless Situation, and regardless of the accumulating Pressure of the Miseries of the People, which their infatuated Conduct must contribute to increase, are nevertheless still so hardened in their Guilt, as to endeavour to keep alive the Flame of Rebellion in this Province, which will otherwise soon be reinstated in its former Prosperity, Security, and Peace:

Nor can we at present resolve to extend the Royal Clemency to those who are poluted with the Blood of their Fellow Citizens, most wantonly and inhumanly shed under the mock Forms of Justice, because they refused Submission to an Usurpation which they abhorred, and would not oppose that Government with which they deemed themselves inseparably connected: And in order to give Quiet and Content to the Minds of his Majesty's faithful and well affected Subjects, WE do again assure them, that they shall have effectual Countenance, Protection and Support, and as soon as the Situation of the Province will admit, the Inhabitants will be reinstated in the Possession of all those Rights and Immunities which they heretofore enjoyed under a free British Government, exempt from Taxation, except by their own Legislature: And we do hereby call upon all his Majesty's faithful Subjects to be aiding with their Endeavours, in order that a Measure, so conducive to their own Happiness, and the Welfare and Prosperity of the Province, may be the more speedily and easily attained.

GIVEN under our Hands and Seals, at Charles-Town, the First Day of June, in the Twentieth Year of His Majesty's Reign and in the Year of Our Lord One Thousand Seven Hundred and Eighty.

HENRY CLINTON,

MARIOT ARBUTHNOT.

By their EXCELLENCY's Command,

JAMES SIMPSON, *Secretary.*

CHARLES-TOWN: Printed by ROBERTSON, MACDONALD & CAMERON, in Broad-Street, the Corner of Church-Street.

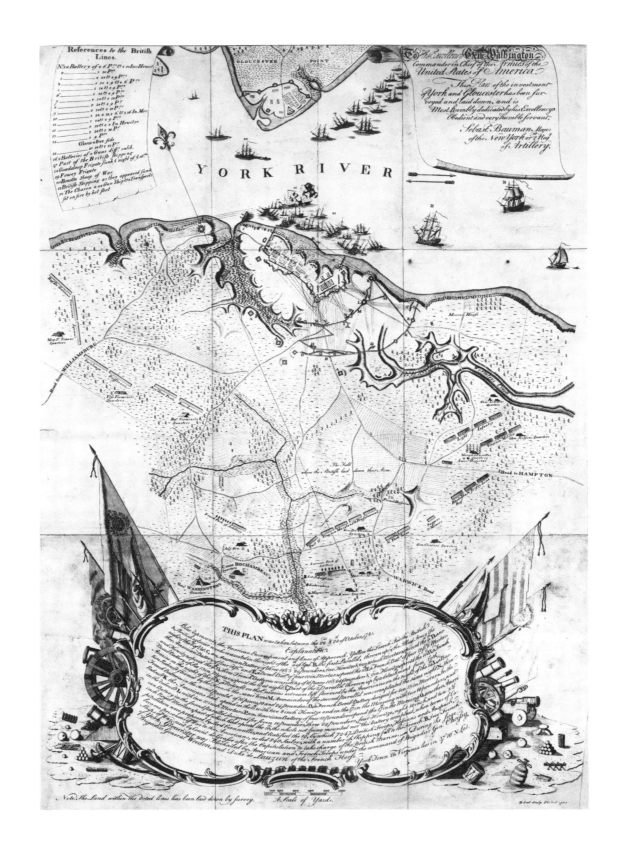

Disposition of the American and French forces, including the
headquarters of both Washington and Rochambeau, facing
Cornwallis at Yorktown. From the Rochambeau Collection.

This hand-colored etching depicts the surrender of the British
troops at Yorktown on October 20, 1781. Off the coast in
Chesapeake Bay lies the French fleet, commanded by Admiral de
Grasse.

Reddition de l'Armée Angloises Commandée par Mylord Comte de Cornwallis aux Armées Combinées des Etats unis de l'Amerique et de France aux ordres des Generaux Washington et de Rochambeau a Yorck town et Glocester dans la Virginie le 19 Octobre 1781 Il s'est trouvés dans ces deux postes 6000 hommes de troupes reglées Angloises ou Hessoises et 22 Drapeaux 1500 Matelots 160 Canons de tout Calibre dont 75 de Fonte 8 Mortiers 40 Batimens dont un Vaisseau de 50 Canons qui a eté Brulé 20 Coudes Bas. Ce jour a jamais memorables pour les Etats unis en ce quil asura definitivement leurs independances.

A. Yorck Towwn   *C Armées Angloise sortant de la place*   *E. Armée Francoise*   *G Armée naval de France aux Ordres du Comte de Grace*   *I. Riviere d'Yorck*
B. Glocester   *D. Les Armes des ennemis posée en Faisceaux*   *F Armée Ameriquaine*   *H Baye de Chesapeack*

69

Charles Cornwallis, commander of the British army in the Southern states, 1780–81, had participated in earlier battles in Long Island, New Jersey, and Pennsylvania. Engraving in John Andrews, History of the War with America, France, Spain, and Holland . . . (London, 1785). LC-USZ62-45340

The first and last pages of the Articles of Capitulation at Yorktown, agreed to on October 19, 1781, by Lord Cornwallis, commanding the British army, and Captain Thomas Symonds, the senior naval officer. From the Washington papers.

delivered up in their present State, to an Officer of the Navy, appointed to take possession of them — previously unloading the private property, part of which had been on board for security during the Siege.

Article 14th.

No Article of the Capitulation to be infringed on pretext of Reprisals, & if there be any doubtfull Expressions in it, they are to be interpreted according to the common Meaning & Acceptation of the Words.

Done at York in Virginia this 19th day of October 1781

Cornwallis
Thos Symonds.

Article 14th.

Granted.

Nathanael Greene, having served simultaneously as a battlefield general and quartermaster general of the Continental army, was Cornwallis' principal opponent in the Southern battles that led to Yorktown. Engraving by James Trenchard, in The Columbian Magazine *(September 1786). LC-USZ62-45507*

Daniel Morgan, whose career in the Continental army advanced from captain to brigadier general, served with Benedict Arnold in the attack on Quebec and with Horatio Gates at Saratoga. In January 1781, at Cowpens, S.C., he turned a retreat from Lt. Col. Banastre Tarleton's British Legion into a stunning victory. Engraving by J. F. E. Prud'homme, based on a sketch by John Trumbull. LC-USZ62-16371

Banastre Tarleton, British army officer, whose cavalry charge coupled with a bayonet attack at Waxhaw, S.C., in May 1780 made his name anathema to the Americans. Engraving in The Westminster Magazine (March 1782). LC-USZ62-45487

The Treaty of Peace

The consequences of Yorktown were felt decisively in London several months later when Parliament refused to continue support of the ministry of Lord North; in March 1782 a new government came to power prepared to open negotiations with the Americans. Even before the allied victory at Yorktown the Continental Congress had appointed a commission consisting of John Adams, Benjamin Franklin, John Jay, Thomas Jefferson, and Henry Laurens to negotiate a peace with Great Britain. (Jefferson never participated, and Laurens, who had been imprisoned in the Tower of London, arrived in Paris only in time to sign the preliminary document.) On November 30, 1782, a preliminary treaty was agreed to; in February 1783 the British proclaimed a cessation of hostilities; and in April Congress followed suit.

On September 3, 1783, in Paris, the American and British commissioners signed the Definitive Treaty of Peace, and the United States took its place as a free and independent state among the family of nations.

The appointment by the Continental Congress on July 4, 1776, of a committee "to prepare a device for a Seal of the United States of America" initiated several years of discussion on its design. In 1782 the Secretary of Congress Charles Thomson did the drawing shown here. After some revisions by William Barton, a Philadelphian whose design for the reverse of the seal was accepted as he had drawn it, the seal was adopted in Congress on June 20, 1782. Courtesy of the National Archives.

Consequences of the Revolution

Men who participated in the Revolution could not agree about precisely what it accomplished, aside from the obvious fact of independence, and historians are still quarreling about its results. Scholars generally agree that the Revolution, unlike the two other great revolutions of modern times, the French and the Russian, was not launched or sustained by the desire to produce profound social and economic change. Earlier in this century historians believed that the Revolution had resulted in a more equitable distribution of property throughout America, but later, more careful study has shown that it merely arrested for a short time a gradual, long-range trend toward greater inequality in the distribution of wealth. On religion, however, the impact of the Revolution was considerable. Established churches were put on the defensive, with equality of treatment for all denominations being demanded and, in most cases, granted. On education, public and private mores, the political milieu, the family, and a host of other institutions and attitudes the impact of the Revolution is still not clear, although scholars are searching assiduously for answers.

The Revolution changed the status of persons little. In particular, the status of blacks it changed hardly at all. In some northern states, it is true, the wheels of emancipation were put in motion, but the great mass of Negroes remained in bondage. Yet the promise of the Declaration of Independence, that all men are created equal, acted as an acid on the American consciousness, slowly, at times imperceptibly, eating away the tolerance for slavery until its inhuman edifice collapsed. That the promise of the Declaration of Independence has not yet been fully realized is a measure of the imperfection of the American Revolution. That that promise still prods the national consciousness, that it is still a catalyst for progressive change, is the enduring triumph of the American Revolution.

The exhibit as well as the publication of this catalog are joint endeavors of the Exhibits, American Revolution Bicentennial, Information, and Publications Offices under the direction of the Assistant Librarian of Congress. The catalog was produced through the Verner W. Clapp Publication Fund.